HOW TO USE OSCILLOSCOPES
AND OTHER TEST EQUIPMENT

OTHER TITLES OF INTEREST

HOW TO USE OSCILLOSCOPES
AND OTHER TEST EQUIPMENT

by
R. A. PENFOLD

BERNARD BABANI (publishing) LTD
THE GRAMPIANS
SHEPHERDS BUSH ROAD
LONDON W6 7NF
ENGLAND

PLEASE NOTE

Although every care has been taken with the production of this book to ensure that any projects, designs, modifications and/or programs, etc., contained herewith, operate in a correct and safe manner and also that any components specified are normally available in Great Britain, the Publishers do not accept responsibility in any way for the failure, including fault in design, of any project, design, modification or program to work correctly or to cause damage to any other equipment that it may be connected to or used in conjunction with, or in respect of any other damage or injury that may be so caused, nor do the Publishers accept responsibility in any way for the failure to obtain specified components.

Notice is also given that if equipment that is still under warranty is modified in any way or used or connected with home-built equipment then that warranty may be void.

First Published – October 1989
Reprinted – August 1991
Reprinted – July 1993
Reprinted – February 1996

British Library Cataloguing in Publication Data
Penfold, R. A.
    How to use oscilloscopes and other test equipment
      1. Electronic testing equipment
      I. Title
      621.3815'48

ISBN 0 85934 212 3

Printed and bound in Great Britain by Cox & Wyman Ltd, Reading

Preface

Anyone who develops an interest in electronics as a hobby soon realises the importance of having a few items of test equipment. Things can and do go wrong from time to time, and electronics projects are very unforgiving if even the most minor of errors are made. Trying to track down something as simple as a cracked printed circuit track can be very difficult and time consuming without the aid of some test equipment. There is a wide range of test equipment available these days, and much of this is at prices within the range of many electronics hobbyists. The main questions that face someone setting up an electronics workshop are what equipment is relevant to their needs, what can the various items of test equipment be used for, and how can they be used to good effect in practice?

This book aims to answer these questions, and is primarily concerned with oscilloscopes. Chapter 1 deals with the basics of oscilloscopes, including their basic function, their controls and facilities, and advice on buying a suitable instrument. Chapter 2 is concerned with using an oscilloscope to test various types of circuit, including digital and linear types. The third chapter deals with other items of equipment, including logic probes, pulsers, signal generators, digital frequency meters and component testing. The capabilities and limitations of these units are discussed, together with some advice on what to buy and how to set about using them for fault finding. The obvious omission is the multimeter, but this all-important piece of test equipment is covered in two other books (BP239 and BP265), by the same author and publisher.

R. A. Penfold

Warning

Never make tests on any mains powered equipment that is plugged into the mains unless you are quite sure you know exactly what you are doing.

Remember that capacitors can hold their charge for some considerable time even when equipment has been switched off and unplugged.

Contents

Chapter 1

OSCILLOSCOPE BASICS

An oscilloscope is almost certainly the item of test equipment most coveted by the majority of electronics enthusiasts. Although an oscilloscope tends to be regarded by many as a sort of universal panacea for all electronic ills, this is a rather over optimistic view of an oscilloscope's capabilities. There are very definite limitations on what one of these units, even a high specification type, can achieve. There are types of circuit where testing using an oscilloscope is likely to be of very limited value. However, in general an oscilloscope will tell you what you want to know, and will unquestionably prove to be more flexible than any other item of test equipment you buy.

For the electronics hobbyist there are two main drawbacks to an oscilloscope. One is simply that the cost of a good modern workshop instrument is likely to be quite high, at about ten times the price of a medium priced digital multimeter. Modern laboratory grade instruments are even more costly, but are probably highly over-specified for most amateur requirements anyway. Whether or not the cost of a workshop oscilloscope is something that you can justify obviously depends on individual circumstances, including how much spare cash you have, and how much use the unit is likely to get.

The second problem is a lack of information on how to use an oscilloscope. Much of the published information, including the manuals provided with most instruments, is strongly biased towards the professional user. Some of the information is relevant to the electronics hobbyist, but much of it is not.

This book is aimed fairly and squarely at the electronics hobbyist who has bought an oscilloscope but is having difficulty in fully exploiting it, or who is considering the purchase of an oscilloscope but is uncertain what to buy and what can be achieved with the less expensive models. The final chapter covers several other types of test gear, but this publication is mainly concerned with oscilloscopes. The subject of multimeters is not included here, because there are two books in our range devoted to these (BP239 "Getting The Most From Your Multimeter", and BP265 "More Advanced Uses Of The Multimeter").

C.R.T. Basics

The basis of an oscilloscope is the cathode ray tube (c.r.t.). At least, until recently it was the basis of an oscilloscope. These days there are alternatives such as l.e.d. and l.c.d. screens. However, the vast majority of oscilloscopes are still based on the traditional c.r.t. rather than modern semiconductor screens. While the circuits used with these modern semiconductor screens are very different to those used to drive a c.r.t., the differences are largely hidden from the user. The controls are much the same, and the display should show the same trace. Here we will only consider conventional c.r.t. based oscilloscopes since these are the ones most of us will be using for the foreseeable future. Instruments which have semiconductor screens operate in a somewhat different manner, but provide the same effect, and are used in exactly the same manner.

A c.r.t. is much more like an electronic valve than a modern semiconductor device. Those who can remember what valves look like will recall that they are a bit like light bulbs with some additional electrodes. The filament is needed to heat the device's cathode, and the heat has the effect of exciting the electrons in the cathode so that some of them become detached from it. In the most basic of valves, the only other electrode is the anode, and if a voltage of the correct polarity is connected across the anode and the cathode (negative supply to the cathode), an electron flow from the cathode to the anode will result. If the signal applied to the valve has the wrong polarity, no current will flow since the anode is cold, and will not emit a significant number of electrons. It is presumably from this one way flow of electricity that the "valve" name is derived. In this form the device gives much the same basic action as a semiconductor diode or rectifier.

In a cathode ray tube the heated cathode is retained, but the anode is replaced by a relatively complex set of electrodes that are designed first to focus the electrons from the cathode into a narrow beam, and then to direct them in the required

2

direction. The electrons strike a phosphor screen at the front of the component, and at the point they strike the screen a spot of light is produced. Due to the narrowness of the electron beam, this spot is very small in diameter. In fact it can usually be focused down to about one millimetre in diameter, and possibly even less than this.

By controlling the direction of the beam it can be aimed at any point on the screen, and the spot of light can therefore be moved to any desired point on the screen. There are two methods of deflecting the beam, which are to use an electromagnetic force or an electrostatic one. While the former of these is the standard one for television sets and monitors, the electrostatic method is the one normally used in c.r.t.s intended for operation in oscilloscopes. This method is basically very simple, and it just requires four plates mounted between the focusing electrodes and the screen. These comprise one plate near the top of the screen, one near the bottom of the screen, and one to either side of it. The ones above and below are the "Y" plates, while those to either side are the "X" plates.

With no voltage difference across either set of plates the electron beam carries straight on without being deflected. It therefore hits the centre of the screen. If a voltage difference is placed across the X plates, the beam will be deflected to one side. Whether it is shifted to the left or to the right of the screen depends on the polarity of the voltage, and the amount of shift is dependent on the amplitude of the voltage (and is proportional to it). Starting with a strong negative voltage (i.e. right plate negative), then steadily reducing it to zero, switching polarity, and then steadily increasing the voltage, has the effect of sweeping the spot of light across the screen from left to right. Doing the same thing with the Y plates has a similar effect, but moves the spot of light from the bottom of the screen to the top. Applying a signal to both sets of plates permits the spot of light to be controlled in both planes simultaneously. For example, applying the signal above to both sets of plates moves the spot diagonally across the screen from the bottom left hand corner to the top right hand corner.

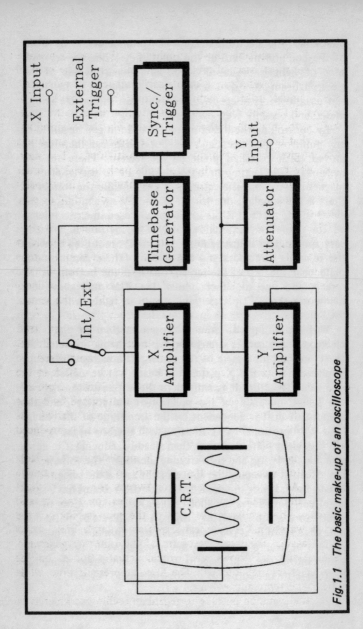

Fig.1.1 The basic make-up of an oscilloscope

4

Scope Basics

A c.r.t. plus suitable power supplies etc. does not constitute even the most basic of oscilloscopes, and can not be used to view signal waveforms. A usable oscilloscope in its most basic form would utilize a setup something along the lines of Figure 1.1. The most important addition here is the timebase section which drives the X plates via the X amplifier. Note that both sets of c.r.t. plates are preceded by amplifiers which give the instrument usable sensitivities. The c.r.t. typically requires a few hundred volts peak to peak in order to fully drive its plates, whereas the input signals will normally be no more than a few volts peak to peak, and could be only about one millivolt peak to peak.

The timebase generator is basically a linear sawtooth waveform generator, or "ramp" generator as it is alternatively known. This generates a voltage which starts at zero, and rises at a linear rate until a certain threshold voltage is reached. The signal then falls back to zero and then starts rising at a linear rate once again. In terms of the spot of light on the screen, this results in it being swept across the screen from left to right at a constant speed. When the spot reaches the right hand edge of the screen it is immediately switched back to the left hand edge, and another sweep of the screen is commenced. In practice the time taken for the spot to be swept back to the left hand edge of the screen can be quite significant, especially at higher sweep rates. This is usually counteracted by having the electron beam blanked during the "flyback" period. As the beam is switched off, no trace on the screen is produced during this period.

The input signal is fed to the Y amplifier via a variable attenuator which enables the sensitivity to be set at a suitable level. As the timebase generator sweeps the spot of light across the screen, the input signal moves the spot up and down. This results in the path of the spot tracing out the input waveform. Figure 1.2 shows an example input waveform against the ramp waveform of the timebase generator, and Figure 1.3 shows what would actually appear on the screen of the oscilloscope. The X axis represents time, while the Y axis represents voltage.

It is a common mistake to regard an oscilloscope merely as

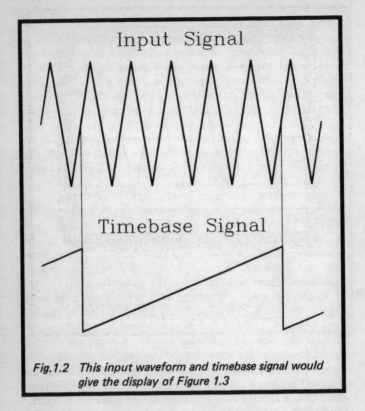

Fig.1.2 *This input waveform and timebase signal would give the display of Figure 1.3*

an instrument for viewing waveforms. It also acts as a measuring device which can measure both duration and signal voltages. The screen of an oscilloscope is fitted with a graticule, which is merely a piece of clear plastic or glass which is marked with lines at what is almost invariably 10 millimetre intervals. These lines are marked on both the X and Y axis. Additionally, the main X and Y axis are marked at what is usually 1 or 2 millimetre intervals. The screen markings in Figure 1.3 show a typical graticule.

In practice the sweep speed can be set at a certain time per division. Note that a "division" in a specification sheet usually means the main 10 millimetre divisions and not the

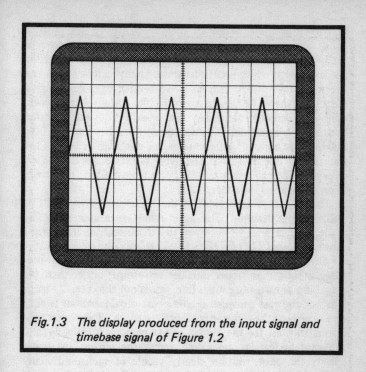

Fig.1.3 The display produced from the input signal and timebase signal of Figure 1.2

smaller 1 or 2 millimetre types. If the sweep speed is set at (say) 100 milliseconds (0.1 seconds) per division, and two points of significance in a waveform are 33 millimetres apart, then you know that they are separated in time by 330 milliseconds (0.33 seconds).

With a repetitive waveform you can easily work out the frequency of the signal after first measuring the duration of one cycle. The frequency of the signal is simply the reciprocal of the duration of one cycle (i.e. divide one by the duration of one cycle). As an example, suppose that the duration of one cycle is measured at 15 milliseconds (0.015 seconds). Dividing 1 by 0.015 gives an answer of 66.66Hz. With medium and high frequency signals it can often be easier to perform the calculation with the duration in milliseconds or microseconds, which gives an answer in kilohertz and megahertz respectively.

Highly accurate frequency measurements are not possible using this method because an oscilloscope provides what is really only a fairly crude analogue readout. This limits the accuracy with which duration measurements can be made, and the same sort of accuracy as that provided by a good digital frequency meter (d.f.m.) is not possible. However, results are still good enough for many purposes. You can optimise accuracy by measuring the duration of several cycles, and then dividing the answer by the number of cycles so as to give the duration of one cycle. Alternatively, where possible choose a sweep speed that results in one cycle almost filling the screen from one side to the other.

The Y axis is calibrated on the basis of so many volts or millivolts per division. This again enables measurements to be made, with a level of accuracy that is perfectly adequate for most purposes.

Although it might seem that an oscilloscope merely provides a spot that traces out the waveform, rather than the waveform shown as a proper line, this is not the case. At least, it is not the case provided the timebase provides about twenty five sweeps of the screen per second, or more. The action then occurs too fast for the human eye to perceive it properly, and the spot appears to be a line across the screen. At lower speeds the spot will be clearly visible as such, and many oscilloscopes are not at their best at slow sweep rates.

Most oscilloscopes have a blue/green medium persistence c.r.t. As the name implies, the persistence of a c.r.t. is a reference to how long (or otherwise) the screen remains glowing after the spot has moved on to a new position. With the usual medium persistence type, this time is quite short, at what is mostly just a matter of a few milliseconds. The trace at slow sweep speeds therefore seems to be a bright dot moving across the screen trailing a short line behind it. This is not to say that at slow sweep rates the input waveform can not be seen. It can usually be seen reasonably clearly, but a spot and short line type display makes it relatively difficult to make a detailed examination of a complex waveform.

There are means of obtaining improved results at low sweep speeds. The most simple of these is to have an instrument which is fitted with a long persistence tube. These usually give a green/yellow trace which does not decay for several seconds. Many long persistence tubes also have a blue short persistence phosphor. At higher sweep rates and with a changing input waveform, with a long persistence tube results tend to be very confusing. It is easy for the display to build up to the point where practically the entire screen is glowing! With a dual persistence tube the idea is to use the green/yellow trace at low sweep rates, and to ignore the blue trace. At high sweep speeds it is the green/yellow trace that is ignored and the blue one that is used. Although there can be advantages to tubes of this type, or to a straightforward long persistence type, they do not seem to be very popular in practice. A long or long/short persistence c.r.t. might be offered as an option, but in most cases there is a Ford-like choice of any screen colour provided it is blue/green and medium persistence.

Another method of obtaining improved performance at low sweep speeds is to have a storage oscilloscope. There are two totally different types of storage oscilloscope, one of which uses a special form of c.r.t. which can hold the trace for a considerable period of time if required. The second type, known as a digital storage oscilloscope, uses semiconductor memory circuits and digital techniques to store a waveform. It is then played back into what is essentially an ordinary oscilloscope. It is played back repeatedly and at high speed so that a proper and entirely flicker-free display is obtained. Instruments which offer these facilities are highly desirable, but are also too expensive to be given serious consideration by most amateur electronics enthusiasts.

Synchronisation

Most oscilloscopes have the ability to operate on a "one shot" or "single sweep" basis. This is where an input signal above a certain level results in the timebase generator being triggered, and a single sweep of the screen being produced. This can be used to view intermittent waveforms or genuine one-off events. The relatively short persistence of most oscilloscope screens means that the view obtained of one-off or infrequent events is often not a particularly good one. With very short signals and high sweep speeds there can be a problem of low trace brightness, even with the brightness control set at maximum.

9

However, careful scrutiny of the screen will normally tell you what you want to know.

Usually the trigger signal is derived from the Y input signal. However, most oscilloscopes have an external trigger socket, and can be switched to trigger from a signal applied to this socket. This is not the sort of feature you will need to use every day, but it can be useful on occasions. It is a feature that is mainly used when you wish to know what is happening at one point in a circuit when a pulse that can be used for triggering purposes occurs at some other point in the circuit. This is a facility that is probably of most value when testing digital circuits. For instance, when testing a parallel printer output it could be useful to know the state of data and handshake lines during and immediately after the strobe pulse. This could be accomplished by triggering the timebase from the strobe line, and viewing the waveform on each of the other lines in turn.

With a repetitive waveform the trigger circuit ensures that the timebase and the input signal are properly synchronised. It is important that each sweep commences at the same point in the waveform. It is essential that the timebase does not simply free-run, as this would give either a "moving" trace, or a completely scrambled and unusable display. Figure 1.4 shows what happens if the sweep commences at a different point in the waveform on successive sweeps, with no form of synchronisation. Each sweep produces the trace slightly offset from the previous one. If the offset is small, the trace will seem to move slowly across the screen. In the example of Figure 1.4 the offset is towards the right, and this is the direction in which the trace will appear to move. With a large offset and even a moderately fast sweep rate, to the human eye the display will appear to be a random jumble of lines.

The trigger circuit activates a new sweep each time a certain voltage is reached, and provided a sweep is not already in progress. Figure 1.5 shows an example input waveform, and the timebase waveform this might produce. This obviously gives the required synchronisation with successive traces laying exactly over each other so that the trace is completely stable. This assumes that the input waveform is unchanging. With a complex input waveform that is not a true

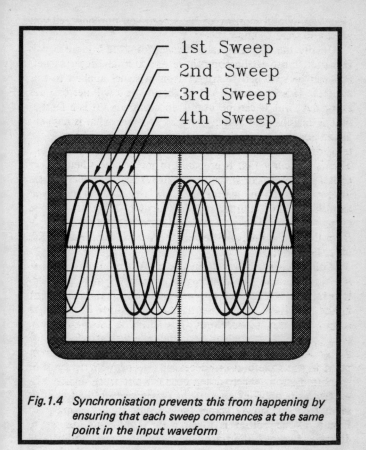

Fig.1.4 *Synchronisation prevents this from happening by ensuring that each sweep commences at the same point in the input waveform*

repetitive type it is obviously not possible to obtain a static display. This form of timebase triggering will then give a display that is as clear and easy to follow as possible. With something like a speech or music signal the rate of change in the signal is often low enough for the human eye to follow what is happening reasonably well. In order to give a usable display from a really fast changing display it might be necessary to set the trigger level quite high so that only intermittent triggering occurs. This will provide you with brief but clear glimpses of the input waveform.

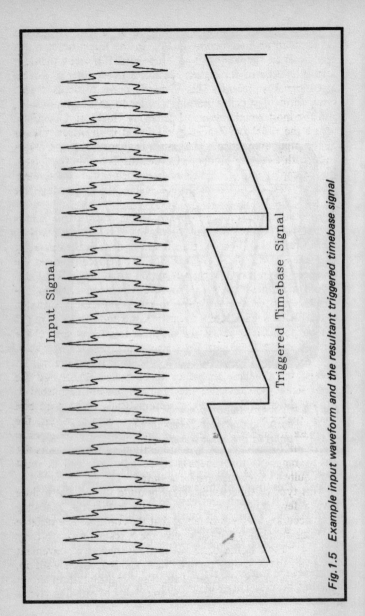

Input Signal

Triggered Timebase Signal

Fig. 1.5 Example input waveform and the resultant triggered timebase signal

Many modern oscilloscopes only seem to have a triggered sweep, with no free-running mode. In the free-running mode the timebase generator is a true oscillator that provides regular sweeps of the screen regardless of whether or not an input signal is present. This obviously needs to be used with some form of synchronisation in order to give usable results, and the most simple means of achieving "lock" is to carefully adjust the timebase frequency so that it is an integer divisor of the input frequency. The result, in theory, is then a stable trace with a certain number of cycles displayed on the screen. For example, with the timebase frequency set at exactly one-fifth of the input frequency, a stable trace showing five cycles would be obtained.

In practice it is not possible to obtain really stable results in this way. Even if the input frequency is totally unchanging, there is bound to be a certain amount of drift in the operating frequency of the timebase oscillator. You carefully adjust the timebase for a stable trace, but within a few seconds the displayed waveform starts to "move"! Even an error in frequency of 0.1Hz is sufficient to give a noticeably unstable trace. With a high input frequency and sweep rate it might not be possible to adjust the timebase frequency control for a really stable trace even for a brief initial period. The solution to this problem is to use a synchronisation circuit that enables the timebase frequency to be pulled slightly by the input signal, so that once the timebase has been adjusted to almost the right frequency, it automatically locks onto and holds precisely the correct frequency. Within reason, the timebase frequency will track up and down with changes in the input frequency. A synchronisation control permits the pull-in range of the timebase to be adjusted, and in most cases quite a wide range can be achieved.

This type of timebase is certainly quite usable, but it does have a few drawbacks. One of these is that the X scaling lacks accuracy. One problem is that the continuously variable timebase frequency tends to make the X scaling very arbitrary anyway. Even if the basic sweep frequency is a convenient one from the X scaling point of view, and is accurately set up, this still leaves a second problem. The synchronisation circuit operates by pulling the timebase frequency to one that gives a

13

stable trace. This can produce a substantial shift in the time-base frequency, and this will obviously compromise the validity of the X scaling.

Another and substantial problem with a free-running time-base is that it can not accommodate large changes in the input frequency. In some cases the pull-in range is not particularly large even with the synchronisation control set at maximum. Even a fairly modest change in the input frequency will then cause lock to be lost, and would necessitate readjustment of the timebase fine frequency control. Some free-running time-bases have a reasonably wide pull-in range, but they can not track large changes in the input frequency. Few can cope with a change in frequency of even 25%.

A triggered timebase does not have this problem. As the input frequency is raised and lowered, more and less cycles appear on the screen, and a stable trace is maintained. Furthermore, the accuracy of the X scaling is left totally unaffected, since the sweep speed is totally unaffected by the frequency of the input signal. It is perhaps not surprising that free-running timebase modes are absent from many modern oscilloscopes, and where triggered and free-running modes are both available, the triggered mode is likely to be the most satisfactory under practically all circumstances.

Do not confuse a free-running timebase with one that has an "automatic triggering" mode. This is effectively a triggered timebase that triggers itself if there is an inadequate input level to produce triggering. Normally an inadequate input level would give no triggering and a blank screen. Automatic triggering is useful as it enables you to see what is going on in the event of an inadequate input level.

Up to Spec.
So far we have only considered oscilloscopes in a largely theoretical manner. In this section we will take a look at specifications, and the sort of performance you can expect from real low cost oscilloscopes. Some aspects of an oscilloscope's specification are pretty straightforward, but others are much less forthright than they might first appear.

One of the more straightforward aspects of an oscilloscope is its tube size. Most low cost instruments used to have a 2.5

14

or 3 inch diameter tube, but these days you mostly get a more generous 100 by 80 millimetres screen size, with some units now offering a very generous 150 by 120 millimetre screen area. In general, the bigger the screen the better the display quality, and the greater the accuracy with which measurements can be made. A fairly large screen therefore has to be considered an asset, and it is worth paying a certain amount extra for it. A decent screen area is particularly important for multi-trace instruments (a topic which is described in some detail a little later on).

The persistence of the screen phosphor is a subject that has been mentioned previously. In most cases you will probably not have a choice, but if there are two or more options available, the standard green/blue medium persistence type is the safest choice for good all-round performance. A long persistence c.r.t. is probably only worthwhile if you are mainly interested in viewing low frequency signals, or using long sweep times in order to view signal envelopes or something of this nature.

The main specification of an oscilloscope is its bandwidth. In advertising literature you will come across references to something like "low cost 20MHz oscilloscope". There is a maximum frequency to which an oscilloscope can respond properly, and beyond this frequency the response often falls away quite rapidly. The bandwidth quoted in most specification sheets is the $-3dB$ point. Just how important the bandwidth of an oscilloscope will be depends entirely on the type of signals you will wish to investigate. The upper limit of the audio spectrum is 20kHz, and if you are genuinely only interested in audio signals, then quite a modest bandwidth should suffice.

Do not make the common mistake of thinking that you only need a bandwidth that is equal to the highest fundamental input frequency that will be fed to the oscilloscope. The most simple waveform is the sinewave type, and this contains just a single frequency. All other repetitive waveforms are comprised of a fundamental frequency plus harmonics (multiples) of that frequency. Some signals contain strong harmonics at frequencies many times higher than the fundamental, while others contain only a few weak low

15

frequency harmonics. In general, the more rounded a waveform is, and the more gradual its attack and decay, the weaker its harmonic content will be. The faster its rise and fall times, and the more angled it is, the higher the harmonic content is likely to be.

A triangular waveform is not that far removed from a sinewave, and has only a low harmonic content with no higher frequency harmonics at all. A squarewave has very fast rise and fall times, is very angular, and has strong harmonics extending to many times the fundamental frequency. In fact a theoretical squarewave has harmonics that get weaker and weaker at higher frequencies, but which extend into infinity. In practice the switching times of electronic components place a definite limit on the highest harmonic present. A waveform which is short and spiky, like a rectangular pulse signal, is predominantly harmonics with a relatively weak fundamental signal. Figure 1.6 shows the harmonics present, and their relative strengths, for a few common waveforms.

The implication of all this for oscilloscope bandwidths is that in order to accurately display a waveform it might be necessary to have a bandwidth that is ten or more times higher than the fundamental input frequency. On the other hand, if you wish to measure the amplitude of high frequency signals but are not interested in the waveform, or they will only be sinewaves anyway, the bandwidth needs to do no more than accommodate the highest frequency you will wish to measure. For most purposes a bandwidth of 5 to 10MHz is adequate. These days most low cost oscilloscopes seem to offer a bandwidth of about 20MHz. An instrument having a bandwidth much greater than this is likely to be very much more expensive. Unless you really need the extra bandwidth for some reason, or you can find a wide bandwidth instrument at a good price, a standard 20MHz type will be a much more practical proposition.

In addition to the bandwidth, specification sheets often quote a "risetime". With a high speed squarewave input the screen should show an instant rise to the peak level on the rising edge of the waveform. Due to the frequency response limitations of the circuit, the risetime of the displayed signal will be something less than instant, although this may not be

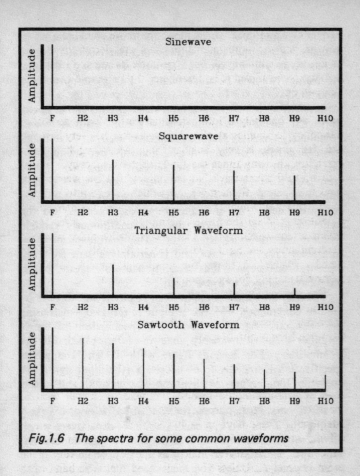

Fig.1.6 The spectra for some common waveforms

apparent unless high sweep speeds are used. The risetime is simply the measured time taken for a high speed input signal to go from its peak negative value to its peak positive one. For a good low cost oscilloscope a figure of around 15 to 20 nanoseconds is typical. When measuring the risetime of a fast signal you need to bear in mind the limitations of the oscilloscope itself, since a lack of apparent speed in the waveform could be largely due to the limitations of the oscilloscope.

17

The sensitivity of an oscilloscope is usually expressed as so many volts or millivolts per division. The maximum degree of sensitivity you will require depends very much on the type of testing you will be undertaking. For most purposes a maximum sensitivity of about 10 millivolts per division will suffice, but when testing low level audio circuits and devices a somewhat higher maximum sensitivity can be advantageous. Fortunately, most modern oscilloscopes seem to have maximum sensitivities of about 1 or 2 millivolts per division, and you are unlikely to need greater sensitivity than this. The Y attenuator should provide a wide range of sensitivities, permitting inputs of up to a few hundred volts peak to peak to be accommodated. At one time most oscilloscopes had the switched attenuator backed up by a continuously variable (volume control style) attenuator. This feature seems to be somewhat rarer these days, and is certainly absent from my present oscilloscope. It is certainly a useful feature, but is one I have managed to live without.

Virtually all oscilloscopes have an X input, and this can be used in conjunction with the Y input to test two signals using the "lissajous" figure method. The specification of the X amplifier is almost invariably somewhat inferior to that of the Y amplifier. For lissajous figure work a high X amplifier specification is unlikely to be necessary (the input signals are normally audio types for this type of checking), and so this state of affairs is quite acceptable.

The standard input impedance for an oscilloscope is 1 megohm. This is shunted by a small amount of capacitance which significantly reduces the input impedance at high frequencies. This input capacitance should be as low as possible so that the input impedance at high frequencies is as high as possible. The input capacitance is usually about 20pF, but overall it is likely to be substantially more than this due to the capacitance of the test leads. The input capacitance will always be significant, and the reduced input impedance at high frequencies is something that must be borne in mind when testing medium or high impedance circuits carrying signals at a few hundred kilohertz or more.

The timebase should cover a wide range of sweep speeds, preferably extending from about 0.5 seconds or more per division to 0.5 microseconds or less per division. A free-running or automatic triggering mode is useful, but is not something I would consider to be essential. A triggered sweep mode is something that I would consider to be essential these days, and an external trigger socket is more than a little useful. It is also helpful if a wide range of switched sweep rates are backed up by a continuously variable control that permits intermediate speeds to be obtained.

Another more than slightly useful facility is a magnification switch. This effectively stretches the waveform by a certain factor, which is usually 5 or 10. This does not simply step up the sweep speed by this amount, but effectively stretches the waveform so that it is too wide to fit onto the screen. A shift control (usually the ordinary X shift type) then enables you to move along the waveform so that any desired part of it can be viewed in detail. The effect is very much as though the display is acting as a moveable "window" that can be shifted from side to side so that the desired part of the waveform can be examined (Figure 1.7). This facility is not of great value with a repetitive waveform where one cycle is very much like the next. However, it is very valuable when examining non-repetitive waveforms if the point of the waveform that is of primary interest is well removed from the point where the timebase is triggered. Simply using a faster sweep speed to get a magnified view would then shift the part of the waveform you wish to examine right off the right hand side of the screen.

The trigger sensitivity is normally given in divisions rather than voltages, since the trigger sensitivity changes when the Y input sensitivity is altered. With most modern oscilloscopes the trigger point can be set practically anywhere on a repetitive waveform.

Extras

Oscilloscopes sometimes have some useful extras included. This could be something as basic as a set of test leads, or it could be some advanced extra facilities such as a range of power supply outputs. Most oscilloscopes are supplied complete with a set of test leads. These will usually only be the basic type which comprise a plug at the oscilloscope end

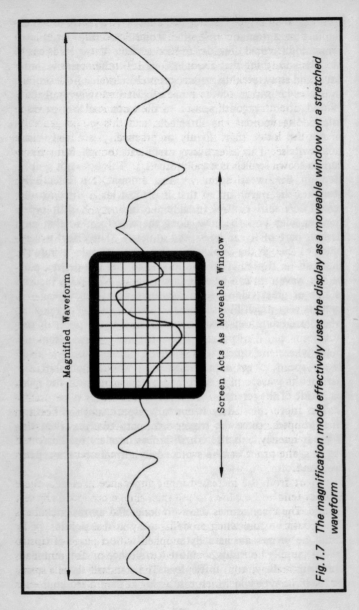

Magnified Waveform

Screen Acts As Moveable Window

Fig.1.7   The magnification mode effectively uses the display as a moveable window on a stretched waveform (usually a BNC type), about half a metre to a metre of screened lead, and then a couple of short insulated leads terminated in crocodile clips. The unscreened section of the leads has to be kept quite short at about 100 to 150 millimetres in order to keep stray pick-up to an acceptable level. At least, the unscreened section of the non-earth lead must be kept quite short. The unscreened section of the earth lead can be made quite long without any ill effects, and this would generally make the leads easier to use in practice. Few ready-made test leads seem to offer a long earth lead though, but making up your own leads is not too difficult.

In common with many users, I buy X10 oscilloscope probes and largely ignore the simple test leads supplied with the instrument (a few oscilloscopes are supplied complete with one probe of this type). The "X10" name of the test probes is perhaps a little misleading as it suggests that the probe boosts the sensitivity of the oscilloscope. In fact the opposite is true, and these probes reduce the sensitivity by a factor of ten. The name is presumably derived from the fact that the sensitivity of the oscilloscope, in terms of volts or millivolts per division, is boosted by a factor of ten (e.g. 10 millivolts per division becomes 100 millivolts per division).

The point of an X10 probe is that it boosts the input impedance by a factor of ten, giving an input impedance of 10 megohms. The input capacitance is substantially reduced, so that the input impedance at high frequencies is also given a boost. The reduction in sensitivity still leaves most oscilloscopes more than adequate in this respect, and the boost in input impedance is very worthwhile, particularly when testing high frequency circuits. These probes have a X1/X10 switch so that the probe can be switched to normal operation when required.

Apart from the increased input impedance provided, these probes tend to be easier to use than simple crocodile clip test leads. The earth lead is relatively long, and a proper probe is a lot easier to use when prodding away at test points. Some of these probes are actually supplied with a range of tips so that they can be easily connected to a range of different leads and terminals without difficulty. The standard tip is a spring loaded clip-on type which can be hooked onto leadout wires

21

etc. if desired. One of the more useful alternative tips is one which enables easy connection to the pins of integrated circuits with no risk of slipping and accidentally short circuiting two pins together.

Some oscilloscopes are equipped with a built-in component tester. This is usually something fairly simple, such as an a.c. signal source which is coupled to the test component, with signals from the component then being monitored using the X and Y inputs of the oscilloscope. This results in various patterns being drawn out on the screen, and from the pattern you can tell whether or not a range of component types are serviceable. A feature of this type is obviously a useful extra, but it is not something I would rate very highly when comparing oscilloscope specifications. My oscilloscope has a component testing facility, but I do not recall having ever used it in earnest!

What is perhaps a more useful feature is the power supply outputs provided by some oscilloscopes. These are primarily intended to power add-ons such as trace multipliers, but they can also be used to power your own circuits. My oscilloscope has +5 volt, +12 volt, and −12 volt outputs, and I have made extensive use of these.

Multi-tracial

The least expensive oscilloscopes are the single trace types. These have a single Y input and can only reproduce one waveform on the screen at a time. These seem to be going out of fashion, and most oscilloscopes now seem to offer some form of multi-trace facility. The two basic types of multi-trace oscilloscope are the dual trace and the dual beam varieties. The better of these two systems is undoubtedly the dual beam type, which utilizes a special c.r.t. which has two electron beams. The two beams are controlled by a common set of X plates, but they have individual Y deflection plates. These plates are driven from two separate Y amplifiers, attenuators, etc. and two waveforms can therefore be displayed on the screen simultaneoulsy. Although a dual beam oscilloscope is superior to a dual trace type in terms of display quality, low cost dual beam instruments seem to be a dying breed. Possibly the dual beam c.r.t.s can not be made at a low enough cost, and the electronics for a dual beam instrument are probably significantly more costly than those for a dual trace type. You may find that a dual beam instrument is not an option that is open to you.

The dual trace system uses what is basically an ordinary single trace oscilloscope to which an internal trace doubler has been added. A trace doubler operates by switching backwards and forwards between two input signals. A d.c. offset is applied to the two signals so that their waveforms are reproduced separately (one above the other) on the oscilloscope's screen.

There are two ways of switching the oscilloscope between the two signals in order to give the required twin traces. One is known as the "alternate" mode, and when this is used the channel 1 signal is coupled through to the oscilloscope on the first sweep, the channel 2 signal is coupled through on the next sweep, then the channel 1 signal on the next sweep, and so on. This system gives what are usually very good quality traces. In fact there is no reason for them to be inferior to a single trace produced on the same instrument. The main drawback of this system is that with sweep frequencies of less than about 50Hz the switching from one trace to the other is clearly visible, and tends to give a rather confusing display.

There is another slight problem in that this system does not guarantee absolutely accurate results. The normal reason for displaying two waveforms simultaneously is to permit their relative phase to be compared. If you look at a repetitive waveform such as a sinewave, you will see that it goes through 180 degrees on the first half cycle, and a further 180 degrees (in the opposite direction) during the rest of the cycle.

Relative phasing is measured in degrees, and if one signal lags another by (say) one quarter of a cycle, there is a 90 degree difference in their phasing (360 degrees divided by 4 = 90 degrees). Measuring the approximate phase difference of two signals is not difficult using a dual trace or dual beam oscilloscope, and in the example shown in Figure 1.8 there is obviously a phase difference of about 180 degrees. The problem with the alternate method of obtaining a twin trace is that the two traces are not produced simultaneously, and the dual trace unit could be introducing a phase difference.

23

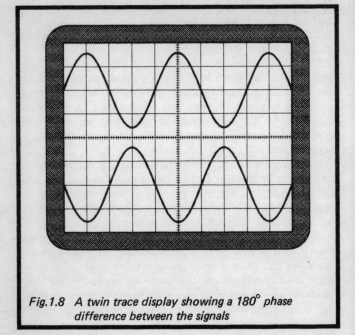

Fig.1.8 A twin trace display showing a 180° phase difference between the signals

In practice this is unlikely to occur, except possibly at very high sweep rates. However, if accurate phase measurements are required, the alternate mode of trace doubling is perhaps not the one to choose.

The other method of trace doubling is the "chopped" mode variety. In this mode the beam is rapidly switched backwards and forwards between the two traces, as in Figure 1.9. As the two traces are produced together on each sweep, there is no chance of the trace doubling introducing phase differences between the two traces. The obvious drawback is that each trace is comprised of a series of dotted or dashed lines, depending on how much higher the chopping frequency is than the input frequency. In practice this is not such a major problem as you might expect. The chopping frequency is not likely to be an exact multiple of the input frequency, and so the bits of the trace that are missing on the

24

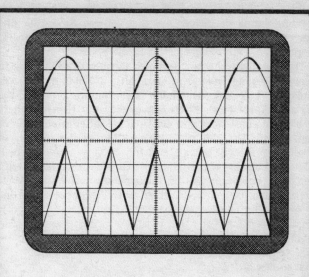

Fig.1.9 Trace doubling by chopping from one signal to
the other. The gaps in the waveforms are not
usually visible in practice

first sweep will not be exactly the same pieces that are missing
in the second and subsequent sweeps. Consequently, the
display is unlikely to show any obvious dotting or dashing
of the two traces.

On the other hand, if the input frequency should happen
to be just right, the chopping action might become apparent.
Most dual trace units these days seem to have a circuit that
tries its best to keep the chopping frequency at a figure that is
not an exact multiple of the input frequency. A sort of anti-
synchronisation circuit in other words. This minimises any
problems with very rough looking traces, or traces with
sections missing. Traces produced by this chopping method
still tend to look slightly inferior to a non-chopped trace
though, presumably due to limitations in the switching speed
of the trace doubler circuit and the oscilloscope itself. Despite
this, the accuracy of the chopped mode makes it the more

popular of the two types of trace doubling. Ideally both methods should be included so that you can choose the one which is most suitable for the testing you are undertaking at the time.

These methods are not restricted to trace doubling, and in theory it is quite possible to have half a dozen or more traces displayed. In practice, the more traces that are produced the greater the problems with display quality etc. However, there are a few oscilloscopes now available that offer three traces or even more. The ability to measure the relative phasing of three or more signals could certainly be very useful, particularly when testing digital circuits. On the other hand, with twin trace operation you can measure the relative phases of several signals by comparing them to the reference signal one by one. The ability to go beyond twin trace operation is certainly useful, but the lack of such a facility is not likely to significantly limit the usefulness of an oscilloscope.

What to Buy

You are highly unlikely to buy a modern oscilloscope and find that it is not up to scratch. Competition amongst the various manufacturers has led to a steady increase in specifications with little change in prices. In so-called "real terms" oscilloscopes are probably cheaper now than at any time in the past, with much better specifications and facilities. A typical low cost instrument these days offers something like a 20MHz bandwidth, double or triple trace operation, a maximum sensitivity of about 1 or 2 millivolts per division, and comprehensive timebase speeds and facilities. Such a specification should be more than adequate for normal hobbyist requirements. Modern oscilloscopes are also very reliable, and you would be unlucky to encounter any problems within the first few years of ownership. Another factor in favour of a modern instrument is that it is likely to be quite small and reasonably light. This makes it easy to accommodate in a spare bedroom workshop.

If you decide to buy a secondhand instrument you need to be very much more careful. Buying a used oscilloscope that is only a few years old is reasonably safe. Provided you check that the unit is in good working order and shows no obvious signs of misuse, you should get a reasonable bargain. If you are not likely to use an oscilloscope a great deal, there is a lot to be said in favour of buying a modern secondhand instrument. The lower cost is more easily justified, and although the lifespan of the instrument will be less than that of a new one, it will probably last a great many years if it receives only a moderate amount of use. Your only problem might be in tracking down a good unit at a realistic price.

Buying an old secondhand oscilloscope is a much more risky business, and something that it is difficult to recommend. You may get an instrument with an amazingly high specification at quite a low price, but as with most things in life, you only get what you pay for. Although the oscilloscope might provide extremely good results, there are a few potential difficulties. One of these is simply the size and weight of older instruments. They are based on valve circuitry, and mostly have very heavy gauge steel cases and chassis. This tends to make them extremely large and heavy indeed. They are intended to be used on heavy-duty work benches, or on special oscilloscope trolleys if it will be necessary to move them around. The average kitchen table or computer/office desk is not strong enough to take one of these instruments, and may well be too small as well.

Even if you are prepared to put up with the size and weight of an instrument of this type, there is still the problem of servicing. An oscilloscope which is a number of years old is quite likely to need servicing several times over a period of years. You might find that spares are not available, or very difficult to obtain. Professional servicing might also be unavailable or difficult to arrange. The main potential problem is the cost of repairs. Although you might have bought the unit quite cheaply, as far as spares and repairs are concerned you have an instrument that costs perhaps more than a thousand pounds when new, and which has spares and service based on the new price. Repairs could easily cost more than buying a replacement oscilloscope! It is easy to find people who have got into difficulties after buying an old secondhand oscilloscope — it is much more difficult to locate satisfied customers. The requests for oscilloscope service manuals and spare parts in electronics publications serve as a warning to the potential difficulties in owning one of these instruments.

In Control

When confronted with your first oscilloscope things can be a bit confusing due to the bewildering array of knobs and switches. However, most of the controls are reasonably straightforward to use, and you should soon become accustomed to them. Here we will consider a representative range of controls, their functions, and how they are used in practice. Obviously the exact controls present on an oscilloscope vary from one instrument to another. Your oscilloscope might not have all the controls mentioned here, and it might have one or two that are not covered in this section. All the important controls of an oscilloscope are described in reasonable detail, and this should tell you all you need to know in order to get started. The manual for your oscilloscope should explain any minor controls that are not detailed here. In any event, you should always thoroughly read the manual for an oscilloscope (or any other item of test equipment) before trying to use it. The manual should clarify any limitations, peculiarities, or special features of the instrument.

The on/off switch is often combined with the brightness control, rather like the on/off switch and volume control of a radio. Although a modern oscilloscope is based on semiconductors, the c.r.t. is a form of valve, and will require the usual warm up time before it becomes fully operational. The brightness control may need a lot of readjustment since the display brightness changes when various types of waveform are displayed. The initial line straight across the screen is brighter than when most waveforms are displayed. The point to bear in mind is that the longer the path of the spot of light, the dimmer the display will become. The trace will not usually have uniform brightness. Parts of the trace where the spot is moving slowly will be brighter than parts where it is moving fast. A squarewave is an extreme example of this effect. The rise and fall times are often so short that the vertical lines are not visible at all, as in Figure 1.10. A very intricate trace using the full height of the screen could give a very dim display unless the brightness control is well advanced.

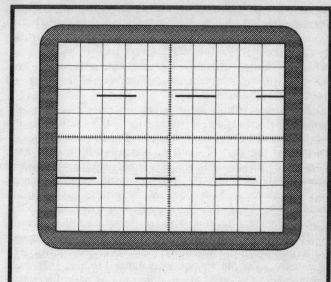

Fig.1.10   The fast risetime of some waveforms, such as this squarewave, results in the vertical sections of the trace being invisible

When displaying very short and intermittent waveforms there is the further problem that the spot of light is only on the screen for a small percentage of the time. This can give a very dim display indeed. On occasions I have been faced with an apparent lack of triggering, only to discover that the waveform was being displayed, but so dimly that it was not visible. With very short sweep speeds and intermittent triggering it is usually necessary to adjust the brightness right up to maximum in order to give a visible display. It is advisable not to set the brightness any higher than is really necessary so as to minimise the risk of "burning" the screen's phosphor coating. Low or moderate brightness usually gives a somewhat better defined display as well.

There will normally be a focus control which is used to focus the electron beam as tightly as possible so that a sharp display is produced. Some oscilloscopes also have an astigmatism control, which is a form of focus control. This is used in conjunction with the focus control in order to obtain optimum display quality over the entire screen. Astigmatism controls seem to be absent from most modern oscilloscopes, which achieve good overall display quality without the need for one (or have a preset astigmatism control that you will probably never need to adjust).

The X and Y shift controls permit the trace to be moved around the screen, and in normal use the Y shift control is adjusted to centre the trace, while the X shift control is adjusted so that the start of the trace coincides with the left hand edge of the screen. With a dual beam or dual trace instrument there should be a separate Y shift control for each channel. Some oscilloscopes have a control that permits the trace to be rotated (but this is often in the form of a preset control). This enables the trace to be accurately aligned with the graticule.

The Y sensitivity is controlled using a switched attenuator plus (possibly) a continuously variable volume control style attenuator. The old way of doing things is to have a relatively low number of switched attenuator positions, with this control operating in perhaps 20dB steps (i.e. each step of attenuation reducing the sensitivity by a factor of ten). This gives rather coarse control, but the volume control style attenuator permits the trace to be adjusted to the required height. Modern instruments usually lack the continuously variable attenuator control, and instead have a switched attenuator having a large number of settings. On my oscilloscope for example, there are twelve levels of sensitivity. These are 2mV, 5mV, 10mV, 20mV, 50mV, 100mV, 200mV, 500mV, 1V, 2V, 5V, and 10V per division. Although this does not seem to accommodate large input voltages, bear in mind that an X10 probe will give 100 volts per division on the lowest sensitivity setting.

Having a large number of switched attenuator settings enables voltages to be measured quite accurately, but the lack of a continuously variable attenuator means that there is no means of adjusting the height of the trace to make optimum use of the screen area. Ideally you should have both features available, but this is a rarity on low cost instruments. If your oscilloscope does have a continuously variable attenuator, bear in mind that the Y calibration is only accurate when this is set for minimum attenuation. With a dual beam or dual trace instrument there should be separate Y attenuator controls for each channel.

Like the sensitivity controls, the timebase sweep speed is usually in the form of a multi-way switch, often using the same 1, 2, 5, 10 sequence of settings as the attenuator switch. This is often backed up by a variable control that enables the gaps to be filled in so that any sweep speed between the maximum and minimum settings of the instrument can be achieved. The X calibration is only valid with the variable sweep speed control set at zero though.

An important control of the timebase section is the trigger level control, or the synchronisation level control. Which type of control your instrument has will depend on whether it has a triggered or free-running timebase. It might have both. The synchronisation level control merely sets the pull-in range of the timebase generator.

The trigger level control might actually be in the form of two controls. One will then be a switch which selects a positive or negative trigger level, and the other will be a potentiometer that sets the trigger level. These days it is more common for the trigger polarity and level to be selected using a single control. This is a potentiometer having a central 0 volt setting. Anticlockwise adjustment sets a negative trigger voltage level, while clockwise adjustment sets a positive trigger level.

The effect of the trigger level control is perhaps best explained with the aid of the waveforms shown in Figure 1.11. In waveform (a) the trigger level has been set at the 0 volt level, and the sweep starts at the 0 volt cross-over point on the waveform. In (b) a strong positive trigger level has been set, and so the sweep does not start until the input signal reaches a suitably strong positive voltage. In (c) the trigger level is a strong negative voltage, and triggering of the sweep does not occur until the waveform reaches almost its peak negative level.

Switches
In addition to the main rotary controls, most oscilloscopes seem to have batteries of slider and push-button switches.

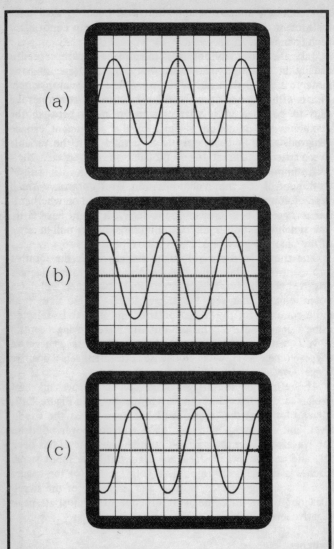

Fig.1.11 The same waveform viewed using three different trigger level settings

These control a number of important functions. Virtually all oscilloscopes, old or new, have the option of using a.c. or d.c. coupling. Where it is possible to use d.c. coupling, this is certainly the better option. Most electronic circuits contain signals that are largely or totally varying d.c. types rather than true a.c. signals. In other words, the signals are always positive with respect to earth (assuming the equipment is of the usual negative earth variety), and are never negative in polarity.

In the simple amplifier circuit of Figure 1.12 for instance, the potential divider at the input (R1 and R2) biases the input and output of the circuit to about 4.5 volts. If the input signal is 200 millivolts (0.2 volts) peak to peak, this gives a voltage at the input of the amplifier that varies from (nominally) 4.4 to 4.6 volts. The voltage gain of the amplifier is about ten times, giving an output voltage of approximately 2 volts peak to peak. The output voltage therefore varies between about 3.5 and 5.5 volts. Using an oscilloscope with

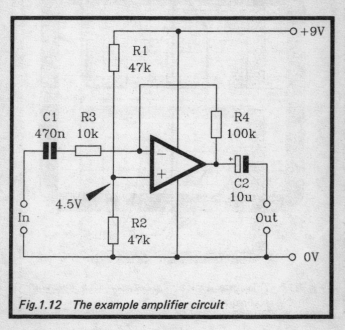

Fig.1.12 The example amplifier circuit

33

d.c. coupling you are not limited to checking that peak to peak signal voltages are as expected. You can measure the varying d.c. voltages in the circuit, which will show up any errors in the biasing.

When using an oscilloscope with d.c. coupling, and assuming that the test circuit does not have dual supply rails, the input will always be positive. If you adjust the trace line to the centre of the screen, you will only be using the top half of the screen. It is better to use the X shift control to move the trace down a few divisions so that most or all of the screen can be used. Figure 1.13 shows the sort of trace that might be obtained with an input signal that is varying between 3.5 and 5.5 volts, with the X shift control adjusted to set the

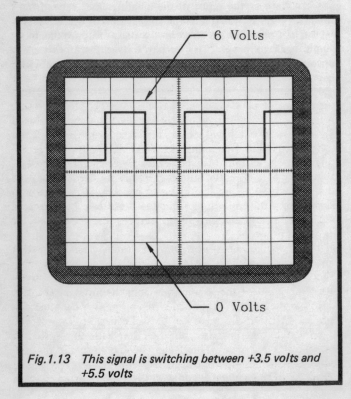

Fig.1.13   This signal is switching between +3.5 volts and +5.5 volts

0 volt level one division up from the bottom of the screen.

A slight problem with a.c. coupling is that it introduces a degree of highpass filtering. The coupling capacitor is usually made quite large relative to the input resistance of the oscilloscope, so that the lower limit of the frequency response is at quite a low figure (typically about 5Hz). This will not usually give any waveform distortion, but it is likely to give slight distortion on low frequency squarewave signals, or any signal of a similar shape. Figure 1.14(a) shows a squarewave as might be displayed using a.c. coupling, while Figure 1.14(b) shows how the same waveform might appear when displayed using d.c. coupling.

Probably the best advice is to use d.c. coupling whenever you are testing what is really a varying d.c. signal rather than a true a.c. type, provided circumstances permit this. If you are trying to measure a very low level signal at the output of an amplifier having a d.c. bias level of a few volts, it might not be possible to do so. The sensitivity would need to be set quite high in order to give a usable display height from the weak signal, but the strong d.c. component on the signal would then tend to take the trace way off the top of the screen. Adjusting the X shift control might enable the trace to be brought back onto the screen, but this is unlikely. When trying to measure something like a few millivolts of noise and ripple on the output of a power supply having an output of about 30 volts d.c., the situation would be even worse. In these situations a.c. coupling has to be used. If you need to know the d.c. levels in the circuit, these can be measured separately using the instrument set for d.c. operation, or using a multimeter.

Many oscilloscopes now have a three position switch offering a.c. coupling, d.c. coupling, or a "ground" setting. The latter short circuits the coupling capacitor, disconnects the input of the Y amplifier from the input socket, and connects it to earth (or "ground" if you prefer the American term). This might seem to be a little pointless, as the oscilloscope can obviously not function with this switch in the "ground" setting. This facility would normally be used when the oscilloscope has been fed with a strong d.c. signal when set to the a.c. mode and with the attenuator set for high

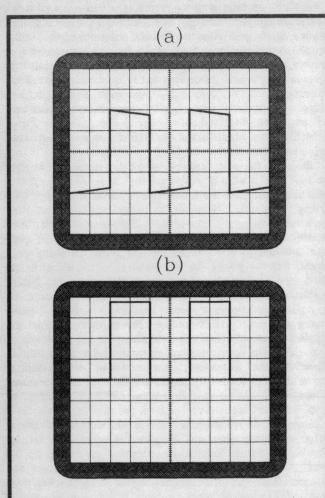

Fig.1.14 Low frequency squarewave input signals with
(a) a.c. coupling and (b) d.c. coupling

sensitivity. This effectively results in the trace shooting about a metre or two off the top of the screen! If you wait long enough the coupling capacitor at the input of the oscilloscope will eventually adjust to the new d.c. operating conditions, and the trace will come back down onto the screen again. The "ground" setting represents a quick way of normalising things and getting the trace back onto the screen. Some X10 probes have "X1", "X10", and something like a "REF" setting. The latter is much like the "ground" setting on the oscilloscope's a.c./d.c. switch.

Oscilloscopes often have a number of switches associated with the sweep generator. A magnification switch is often included, and this is a feature that was described previously. Another option often provided is a +/− switch. Here we are not talking in terms of a switch that determines whether the timebase is triggered on positive or negative half cycles of the input signal, but one which determines whether it is triggered on the rising (+) or falling (−) edge of the waveform. The waveforms of Figure 1.15(a) and (b) show the difference between the two methods of triggering. In (a) the sweep generator is triggered on the rising edge of the waveform, while in (b) it is triggered on the falling edge. In both cases the trigger level control is at the same (positive) level. Figure 1.16(a) and Figure 1.16(b) show the equivalent waveforms but with a negative trigger voltage selected.

If your oscilloscope has an external trigger input, there will be a switch to enable you to select internal triggering or external triggering via this socket. If the unit has dual trace or dual beam operation, there will probably be a switch to select between channel 1 and channel 2 as the synchronisation source when internal triggering is selected. Most oscilloscopes enable the sweep generator to be disconnected from the X amplifier so that an external signal can be applied to the X input. With a dual trace instrument it is quite common to have the channel 2 input function as the X input when this mode of operation is selected.

Further common timebase options are the inclusion of highpass and lowpass filters that can be switched into the signal path of the trigger circuit. These are needed where noise is causing problems with an unstable trace due to the

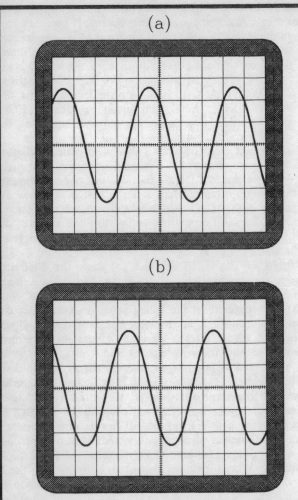

Fig.1.15   Triggering on the positive edge (a) and negative edge (b) of a waveform. In both cases the trigger level is positive

(a)

(b)

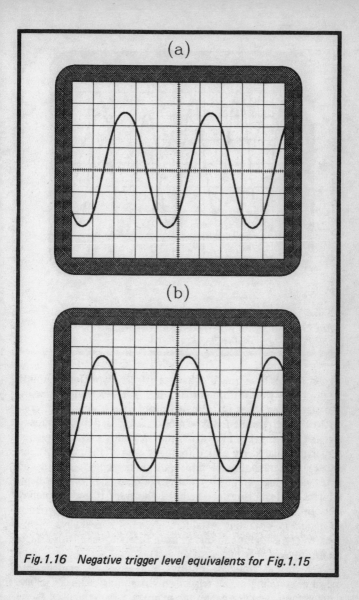

Fig.1.16   Negative trigger level equivalents for Fig.1.15

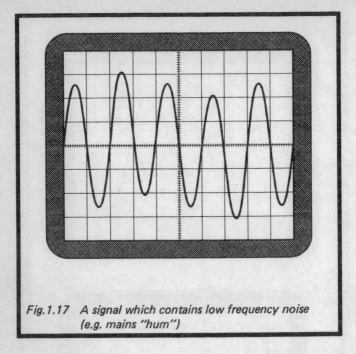

*Fig.1.17   A signal which contains low frequency noise
(e.g. mains "hum")*

trigger circuit operating at what are effectively different points in the input waveform. Actually it is not necessarily noise on the signal that gives this type of problem. A signal that consists of a high frequency type modulated with a low frequency signal (Figure 1.17) or a signal that contains a low frequency signal modulated by a high frequency type (Figure 1.18) can cause problems. Lowpass filtering in the trigger circuit can help when high frequency noise/modulation is the problem, while a highpass filter can stabilise the trace if low frequency noise/modulation is causing problems. If you ever experience problems in obtaining a stable trace, then it is always a good idea to try switching in one or both filters to see if this effects an improvement (which it often will).

Yet further timebase options that might be available are a.c./d.c. coupling in the trigger circuit and a "mains" facility. This second facility enables the mains supply to be used as the

40

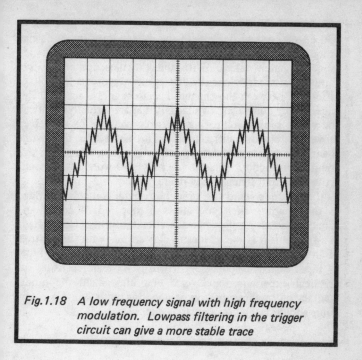

Fig.1.18   A low frequency signal with high frequency
modulation.   Lowpass filtering in the trigger
circuit can give a more stable trace

signal source for the trigger circuit. Presumably this could be useful from time to time, but it is not a feature I have ever used much.

With a dual trace oscilloscope there should be a switch to select single or dual trace operation. There will probably be no option of this type with a dual beam instrument. Usually there are separate brightness controls for each beam, and if only one beam is needed you just fully back-off the brightness control for the one that is not required. If the trace doubler offers both switched and alternate modes of operation, there will probably be a switch so that you can select the desired mode. However, it is possible that the oscilloscope will have automatic switching, with the best mode for the sweep speed in use being selected automatically.

With a dual trace/beam instrument there is sometimes a switch that enables the channel 2 signal to be inverted. This

41

is useful when trying to compare two signals where one is 180 degrees out of phase with the other. Inverting one signal brings them in-phase on the screen so that comparisons are rendered much easier. With some oscilloscopes there is a comparison mode where the displayed waveform is the voltage difference between the channel 1 and channel 2 signals. This is useful for comparing two signals that are virtually identical, and where simply comparing the two waveforms on the screen shows no obvious differences. The ability to invert one channel is very useful for operation in conjunction with this comparison facility, since it will only give worthwhile results if the two input signals are in-phase.

If you understand the functions of the controls described in this chapter, then you are well prepared to go on and actually use an oscilloscope for circuit testing. However, if at all possible it is a good idea to play around with the controls of an oscilloscope for a while, viewing as many different types of input signal as possible. There is no real substitute for practical experience, and once you understand the fundamentals of oscilloscopes, experimenting with one for a few hours should teach you a great deal more.

Chapter 2

IN USE

Once you are conversant with the controls of your oscilloscope, and you understand its capabilities and limitations, you are ready to start testing with it in earnest. A decent workshop oscilloscope can provide useful tests on most types of electronic circuit, and with a little applied technical knowledge it should be possible to get practically any reluctant electronic projects up and running. I would not be truthful if I said that servicing using an oscilloscope required little or no technical knowledge. With any electronic testing, the greater your understanding of the equipment under test the greater your chance of fixing it. On the other hand, you do not need to be a real expert at electronics in order to get some useful results using an oscilloscope. With the aid of an oscilloscope a beginner can soon obtain a much better understanding of how electronic circuits function, and will then be better placed to fully exploit the capabilities of the instrument.

Probably the easiest type of circuit to test using an oscilloscope is a linear type (audio amplifiers, etc.). The only provisos are that the signal frequencies must be within the oscilloscope's bandwidth, and the signal levels must be large enough to produce a usable trace height. Testing something like the input stages of a u.h.f. receiver could prove impossible, but audio stages should be within the compass of any oscilloscope.

Linear Testing

For linear testing an oscilloscope is mostly used as what is really a form of signal tracer. A conventional signal tracer is just a sensitive audio amplifier driving a loudspeaker or headphones, often having a demodulator probe to permit amplitude modulated (a.m.) radio signals to be detected. In use, a signal is supplied to the input of the circuit under test, and this can be supplied by either a signal generator or the normal signal source for the equipment. The signal tracer is used to search for the signal at strategic points in the circuit. There are various approaches to checking the progress of the signal along the signal path, but it basically boils down to starting at the output and working forwards, commencing at the input and working backwards, or jumping in at the middle and then working in a direction that depends on the result of the first test. I generally start at the input, but the middle first technique is the one that is supposed to give the most rapid results.

Whichever method is adopted, the general idea is to find two points in the circuit that are close together; one with a correct signal level and one with an inadequate level. The fault is then at or near the test point which is providing the inadequate signal level. If we assume that the middle first method is to be used, if this gives a proper signal level, then the circuitry from the input to the initial test point must all be functioning correctly. Subsequent tests would therefore be made at later points in the circuit, working steadily towards the output until a point that provides an incorrect signal level is located. If there is an inadequate signal level at the initial test point, then the fault is in the first half of the circuit, and the section from the initial test point to the output is presumably alright.

In fact there could be a multiple fault in the circuit, and there could be a fault in the output section of the circuit. However, it is a matter of taking things one step at a time, and the fault in the early stages of the test circuit would be located first. It is as well to bear in mind that with modern audio circuits there are often overall negative feedback loops which can make it difficult to locate faults using this method. A fault in the feedback circuit can cause an apparent total failure of the entire circuit, or a large section of it. If a circuit has overall negative feedback and seems to be largely inoperative, the feedback circuit should be subjected to close scrutiny.

Clipping

For signal tracing purposes a simple audio amplifier and loudspeaker or headphones has definite limitations. From the volume of the signal and the volume control setting it is possible to roughly gauge signal levels, but accurate measurements of signal levels are obviously not possible. If the problem is distortion rather than a large or total loss of signal, with a signal tracer you can detect the presence or absence of the distortion at the test points, but the nature of the distortion is unlikely to be apparent.

An oscilloscope is much better for signal tracing as it enables signal levels to be measured with quite a high degree of accuracy. By measuring the input and output levels of a stage it is possible to work out its voltage gain. If the problem with the circuit is a mild loss of voltage gain, the accuracy of an oscilloscope should soon reveal the stage that is at fault. Using a signal tracer the problem could be much more difficult to locate. Any significant distortion should show up quite clearly if a suitable test signal is used, and the type of distortion present should be readily apparent. For testing using a signal tracer I favour using the normal input signal as the test signal. For testing with an oscilloscope it is generally better to use a signal generator, usually with the instrument set to provide a sinewave test signal. This will show up any distortion more clearly than a speech or music signal.

An advantage of using the normal input signal for tracing purposes is that it automatically gives a signal at an appropriate level. If you use a signal generator to provide the input signal you must be careful to set a suitable output level. A rather low level is acceptable, but will obviously be relatively difficult to trace, and might give an indistinct trace due to a relatively high noise level. If you find that the focus control will not permit a sharp trace to be obtained, this usually means that the input signal contains a fair amount of "white" noise (i.e. background "hiss").

An excessive signal level will result in the signal being clipped at some points in the signal path. A sinewave input (as in the upper trace of Figure 2.1) would then look more like a squarewave signal (as in the lower trace of Figure 2.1). Just how squared the signal becomes depends on how heavily it is clipped. What happens when clipping occurs is that an output level in excess of the maximum available peak to peak output level is needed. In the example of Figure 2.2 an output level of 10 volts peak to peak is needed in order to faithfully reproduce the input signal. The output stage of the circuit can only produce a signal of about 4 volts peak to peak though. The signal follows the correct voltage levels until the maximum or

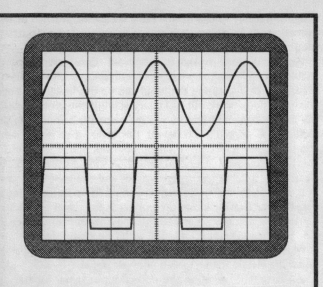

Fig.2.1 Clipping a sinewave input (top) produces virtually a squarewave signal (bottom)

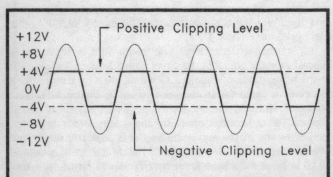

Fig.2.2 Over-driving an amplifier causes the signal to become clipped

minimum output voltage of the stage is reached. It then holds at this level as it can go no further. When the correct output voltage falls back within the range of the output stage, the appropriate output voltage is produced again. With some circuits an excessive input level can result in a malfunction that results in the output voltage going to the maximum level at certain times when it should be at its minimum level, or vice versa. This gives a very severe form of distortion, as shown by the example input and output waveforms of Figure 2.3.

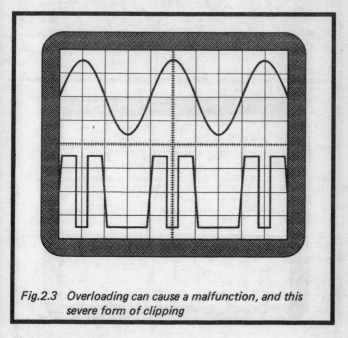

Fig.2.3 Overloading can cause a malfunction, and this severe form of clipping

When testing linear circuits the input level is normally set well below the clipping threshold. Any waveform distortion should then show up quite clearly, and any gain measurements will be accurate. Gain measurements made with the output signal clipped are inaccurate because the output signal can obviously not reach the correct level. Dividing the output signal voltage by the input level in order to give a figure for voltage gain therefore results in an answer which could be well below the true voltage gain of the stage.

One reason for sometimes adjusting the input level just beyond the clipping threshold is to check the biasing of a circuit. Normally the output of an amplifier is biased to about half the supply voltage. Assuming the output stage has reasonably symmetrical output characteristics, this ensures that the positive and negative output clipping levels are more or less the same. This optimises the unclipped output signal level. Some circuits have a preset resistor to permit adjustment of the biasing level, and the best way of adjusting this is to set an output level that only just produces clipping, and then adjust the bias level for symmetrical clipping (Figure 2.4). Figure

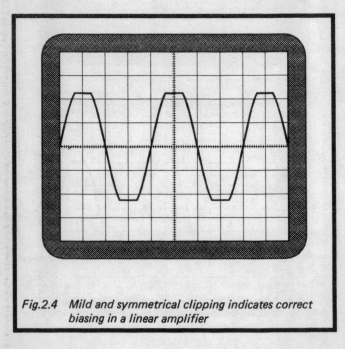

Fig.2.4   Mild and symmetrical clipping indicates correct biasing in a linear amplifier

2.5 (a) and (b) show the waveform that results if the bias voltage is respectively set too high or too low.

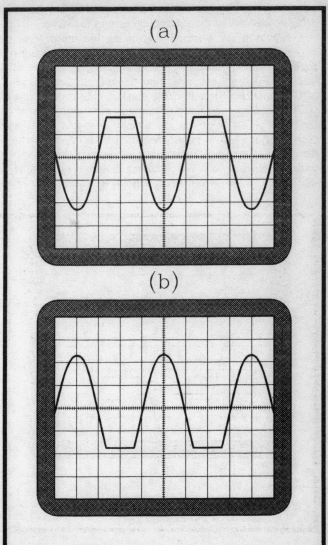

Fig.2.5 (a) Clipping caused by excessive bias level, and (b) the result of an inadequate bias voltage

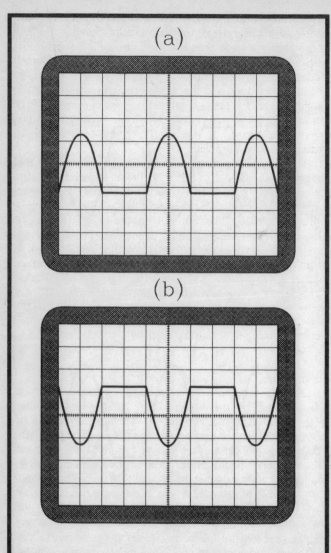

Fig.2.6 (a) The result of no bias voltage, and (b) the result of a bias level equal to the full supply voltage

Frequently when there is a fault in a bias circuit, the result is either zero bias voltage, or one virtually equal to the full positive supply voltage as shown in Figure 2.6. This generally occurs because one of the resistors in the potential divider of the bias circuit has gone open or closed circuit. I suspect that this is not quite true, and that most problems of this type are actually caused by bad joints resulting in one of the bias resistors effectively being absent from the circuit. Testing using an oscilloscope is often a fairly high-tech means of detecting a low-tech problem.

If the biasing of a circuit is incorrect, do not jump to the conclusion that it is one of the biasing resistors that is at fault. There is quite a good chance that this is indeed the cause of the problem, but there are other possibilities. Faulty coupling or decoupling capacitors are not an uncommon source of faults, and these usually manifest themselves in the form of incorrect bias levels. Do not overlook the possibility of a fault in the amplifying device itself, especially if the incorrect bias level is accompanied by a lack of voltage gain. An oscilloscope will normally enable you to narrow down a fault to a small section of the circuit, but it will usually be necessary to back it up with some component or continuity checks in order to find the precise nature of the fault.

Guessing Gains

One slight problem when testing linear circuits is that you often need to know the correct voltage gain for a stage so that any significant error will be noticed. There is no problem of this type if the fault is causing a total break in the signal path, or there is grossly inadequate voltage gain (an error of about 30dB or more). Faults often cause relatively small losses in gain, perhaps unity gain through a stage that should be producing about 12dB of gain. This type of thing can be much more difficult to track down. Simply looking for a break in the signal path is inappropriate, since the signal will be appearing at a high (but slightly inadequate level) at the output of the unit. Things must be taken on a stage by stage basis, with the actual voltage gain being compared with the expected voltage gain.

Many modern linear circuits are based on operational amplifiers, and these pose few problems if you need to estimate the gain of a stage. There are two basic amplifying modes which are the inverting and non-inverting modes. These are shown in Figure 2.7 and Figure 2.8 respectively. Although operational amplifiers were originally designed for use in d.c. amplifier circuits, they are probably used much more in audio and medium frequency circuits these days. Whereas d.c. amplifiers normally require dual balanced supplies, a.c. amplifiers based on operational amplifiers mostly utilize a single supply rail plus biasing resistors and a decoupling capacitor in the feedback network (as in these example circuits).

The innate (open loop) voltage gain of an operational amplifier is very high at d.c. and low frequencies. In use a negative feedback circuit reduces the voltage gain of the circuit as a whole (the closed loop gain) to the required

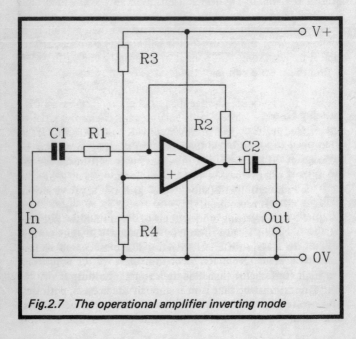

Fig.2.7 The operational amplifier inverting mode

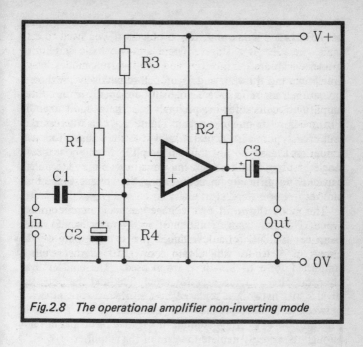

Fig.2.8 The operational amplifier non-inverting mode

figure. In Figure 2.7 the feedback circuit is comprised of R1 and R2, and the closed loop voltage gain is simply equal to R2 divided by R1. For instance, with R2 at 100k and R1 at 15k the closed loop voltage gain of the circuit would be 6.66 times (100/15 = 6.66). There is no need to reach for the calculator when working out closed loop voltage gains. A little mental arithmetic should give a good approximation, which is all that is required.

In the non-inverting mode circuit of Figure 2.8 the negative feedback circuit is again formed by R1 and R2. The mathematics are a little different though. The closed loop voltage gain is equal to (R1 + R2) divided by R1. If R2 is substantially higher in value than R1, then simply dividing R2 by R1 will give an answer that is near enough for present purposes. The non-inverting mode is often used with the inverting input connected direct to the output, and no feedback resistors used. This gives 100% negative feedback and the voltage gain of the circuit is then unity.

Transistor Modes

Guesstimating the voltage gain of a stage which is based on a transistor can be a little more difficult. There are three amplifying modes for transistors, and these are shown in Figure 2.9. The mode shown in Figure 2.9(a) is the common collector type, which is better known as the emitter follower mode. It is easy to spot this mode as it is the only one which has the output coming from the transistor's emitter terminal. There is no difficulty in determining the voltage gain of an emitter follower stage. It is always fractionally less than unity.

The mode shown in Figure 2.9(b) is the common emitter type. This has a large amount of voltage gain, which varies from about 20dB for a low gain device to something well in excess of 40dB for a high gain type. In modern circuits a simplified form of biasing is often used. The emitter then connects direct to the negative supply rail, and the potential divider bias network is replaced by a single resistor connected between the collector and base terminals of the transistor. This introduces a certain amount of negative feedback, but not enough to seriously deplete the gain of the amplifier.

Some common emitter stages provide only quite modest voltage gains. This is where there is an un-bypassed emitter resistance. Sometimes there is a single emitter resistor and no bypass capacitor at all, while in other cases there are two emitter resistors in series, with the bypass capacitor only connected across one of them. The voltage gain is then roughly equal to the value of the collector load resistor divided by the un-bypassed emitter resistance. If the un-bypassed emitter resistance is quite low in value (less than about 150 ohms) this will not give particularly accurate results. The problem is caused by the internal emitter resistance of the transistor. This is typically about 25 ohms (but varies according to the collector current), and must be added to the external emitter resistance in order to give a more realistic answer.

Figure 2.9(c) shows the common base configuration. This is not much used in practice, and is mainly used in v.h.f. and u.h.f. amplifiers. It provides a reasonable amount of voltage

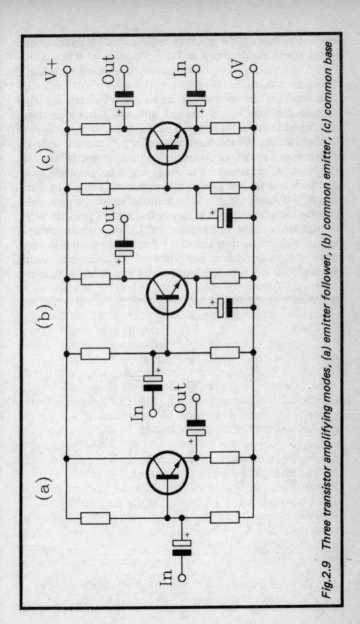

Fig.2.9   Three transistor amplifying modes, (a) emitter follower, (b) common emitter, (c) common base

55

gain, but due to its low input impedance and medium to high output impedance it provides little power gain. It acts a bit like a step-up transformer. This amplifying mode is sometimes to be found in audio amplifiers in the form of half a "long-tailed pair". This is basically just a common emitter stage driving a common base type, and this configuration is often to be found at the input of audio amplifiers.

When testing discrete audio amplifiers you need to keep an eye open for overall negative feedback loops. These are by no means a rarity in audio power amplifiers and pre-amplifiers, and are also to be found in other types of amplifier. Figure 2.10 shows the configuration used in some simple class B power amplifiers. This has a Darlington pair common emitter driver stage (TR1 plus TR2), and complementary emitter follower transistors (TR3 and TR4) in the output stage. Although the current gain of a Darlington pair is very high, the negative feedback via R1 and R2 is likely to be

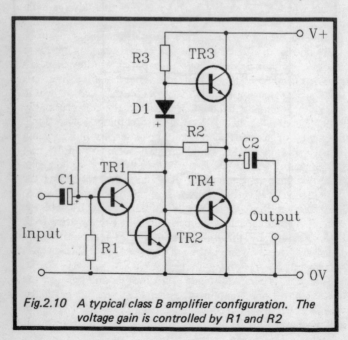

Fig.2.10   A typical class B amplifier configuration. The voltage gain is controlled by R1 and R2

quite substantial, and the gain of the circuit could be quite low (possibly only about 6 times). The voltage gain through the output stage will be the expected unity, but through the driver stage it will only be quite modest. The voltage gain is roughly equal to R2 divided by R1.

Many amplifier configurations do not have the feedback going to the base of the input transistor. Instead it goes from the output to the emitter of the input transistor. With a bit of close scrutiny applied to the circuit diagram you should be able to locate the two feedback resistors and work out the approximate closed loop voltage gain of the circuit. With any configuration that has overall negative feedback, emitter followers still retain unity voltage gain, but the voltage gain of common emitter and common base stages is reduced.

Inverse Tracing

With any form of signal tracing it can be useful to look for signals where there should be none, rather than always looking for a lack of signal in the main signal path. This mainly entails checking the signal present across decoupling capacitors.

Obviously the signal present across a decoupling capacitor should be minimal, since smoothing out unwanted signals is its sole purpose. The decoupling becomes less efficient at low frequencies, and you should bear in mind that slow changes in the voltage across a decoupling capacitor are not necessarily indicative of a fault. If you find something like an audio frequency signal across an emitter bypass resistor in a common emitter stage, then this would certainly seem to indicate that the capacitor is faulty. There is roughly unity voltage gain from the base to the emitter of a transistor, so finding the same signal level at the emitter as at the base would seem to indicate that the transistor is functioning correctly, but the emitter bypass capacitor is open circuit. The negative feedback provided by the un-bypassed emitter resistance would greatly reduce the voltage gain of the stage, probably giving a gain of only about 6dB (two times).

With this type of technique you can sometimes narrow the fault down to one component, rather than just to a particular stage. I would still recommend testing the suspect component whenever this is practical, rather than just throwing it away and putting in a replacement. Apart from anything else, the problem could simply be a bad connection and not a faulty component.

It can be worthwhile checking the signal present on the supply lines. There will normally be a certain amount of noise here, but with audio circuits it should be predominantly very low frequency with little audio frequency signal present. Even a moderate amount of audio frequency signal on the supply lines would suggest that there is a faulty supply decoupling component. It is most likely to be a capacitor that is faulty if there is a significant amount of audio signal. If the signal is a strong very low frequency type, then the supply decoupling resistors should also be checked.

You will often be pointed towards supply decoupling problems even before starting to investigate using the oscilloscope. In some cases faulty decoupling results in negative feedback through the supply lines, and a loss of gain. This is also a symptom of other electronic ailments, and is not of much help. In most cases though, the feedback through the supply lines will be of the positive variety, and will cause low frequency oscillation. This is known as "motorboating", as it often sounds a bit like the engine of a small boat (the slow variety, not a speedboat). If an amplifier exhibits this problem, then the supply decoupling is the first thing you should investigate.

For this type of testing the precise information provided by an oscilloscope is more than a little useful. Although "motorboating" is often caused by supply decoupling problems, it can also be caused by high frequency instability. If the problem is due to a fault in the supply decoupling, then the signal in the main signal path will be a strong low frequency type, with something close to a squarewave being found at virtually every point in the signal path. If the problem is due to high frequency instability, then the waveform will be a modulated high frequency type, probably looking something like the waveform of Figure 2.11. The problem will then be due to something like a high frequency roll-off capacitor that has become faulty (or a "compensation" capacitor as they are often termed these days).

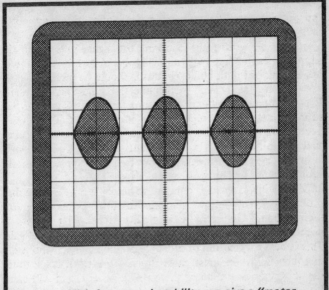

*Fig.2.11   High frequency instability can give a "motor-
boating" type effect*

Squarewave Testing

While a sinewave is probably the best test signal for most
purposes, it can sometimes be useful to use a different
waveform.   Probably the most useful of these alternative
waveforms is the squarewave. As it is rich in harmonics,
and therefore contains a wide range of frequencies, it can be
very revealing.   We have already seen how a lack of low
frequency response can distort a squarewave, producing a
waveform like the upper trace of Figure 2.12. This type of
waveform is actually produced by a combination of low
frequency roll-off and phase shifting.   The lower trace of
Figure 2.12 shows the result of low frequency attenuation
with no attendant phase shifting. In practice it is highly
unusual for roll-off to be provided without any significant
phase shifting accompanying it.   Accordingly, if low frequency roll-off is present it is likely to be the sort of

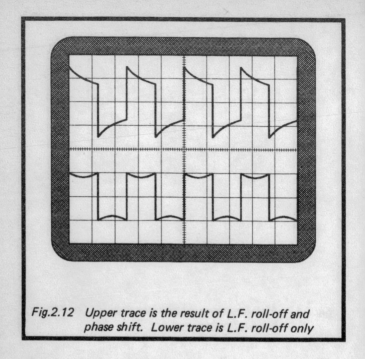

Fig.2.12 Upper trace is the result of L.F. roll-off and
phase shift. Lower trace is L.F. roll-off only

waveform shown in the upper trace of Figure 2.12 that you
will see displayed.

The waveform of Figure 2.13 shows the result of low
frequency phase shifting with no attenuation. This differs
from phase shift plus attenuation in that the horizontal
section of the waveform is a straight line instead of being
curved. Unfortunately, in practice the amount of curve
produced by low frequency attenuation is not very great,
and it can be difficult to differentiate between the two
types of waveform.

Low frequency boost can result in the fundamental signal
being boosted relative to the harmonics. This is obviously
dependent on the fundamental frequency being sufficiently
low, or the boost extending sufficiently high. The effect of a
boosted fundamental frequency is as shown in the upper
trace of Figure 2.14. The lower trace is similar, and is

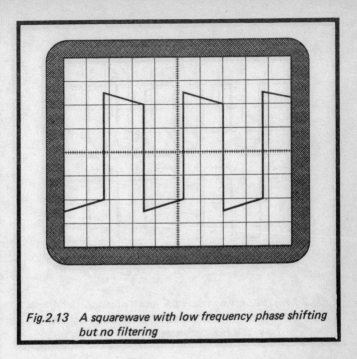

Fig.2.13 A squarewave with low frequency phase shifting
but no filtering

produced by a certain amount of high frequency attenuation
reducing the strength of the upper harmonics. The difference
between the two is that the boosted fundamental gives a
rounded horizontal section of the waveform, whereas the
high frequency attenuation gives a flat-topped waveform.
High frequency attenuation is often accompanied by a phase
shift, giving the slightly different waveform of Figure 2.15.

You can sometimes encounter more exotic waveforms. The
one shown in the upper trace of Figure 2.16 is produced by a
mixture of high frequency attenuation and low frequency
roll-off. The lower trace is one that you are perhaps more
likely to encounter. Here the high frequencies in the squarewave are exciting the circuit into damped oscillation. This is
not desirable since it means the amplifier is on the verge of
oscillation, and "real" input signals could have the same
stimulating effect on the circuit, possibly with an audible

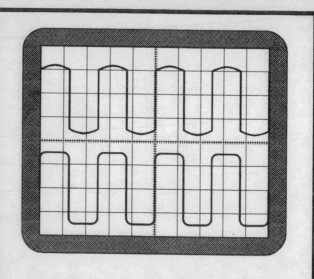

*Fig.2.14   The upper trace is the result of a boosted funda-
mental, while the lower one shows the effect of
reduced H.F. response*

effect on results. This is a problem which is shared by many
audio power amplifiers in varying degrees. Very strong oscillation on a squarewave signal would definitely have to be
regarded as a fault. It could result in damage to the tweeter
in the loudspeaker, especially if the circuits remain oscillating
once the test signal has been removed.

If you apply a squarewave signal to a faulty amplifier you
will sometimes find that the signal found in the later stages of
the circuit is something like the lower trace of Figure 2.17.
The most likely cause of the problem is a faulty coupling
capacitor. A component which should have a value of around
1 to 10μF might actually have a value of just a few picofarads
when faulty.   This very low capacitance, plus the input
impedance of the following stage, forms a highpass filter with
a cut-off frequency of probably a few hundred kilohertz or
more. This results in all but the highest frequency harmonics

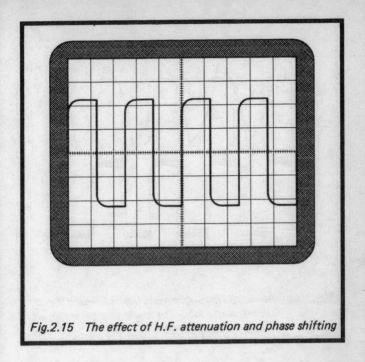

Fig.2.15   The effect of H.F. attenuation and phase shifting

on the squarewave input signal being filtered out, and the resultant waveform is a positive "whisker" on the leading edge of the squarewave, and a negative one on the trailing edge.

Triangle Testing

A triangular waveform is a useful one which is often used instead of a sinewave type. On clipping for example, the pointed peaks of a triangular waveform will show up the waveform distortion at least as well as the rounded peaks of a sinewave. In fact the triangular waveform is probably better for showing very slight clipping.

The straight lines in a triangular waveform are good at showing up any distortion produced by an amplifier. Any lack of linearity will produce kinks or curving of the straight lines. You can not detect very low levels of

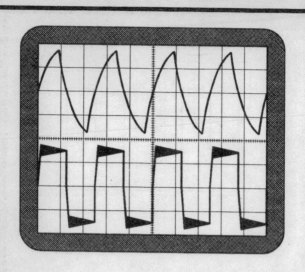

*Fig.2.16   The upper trace is the result of H.F. roll-off and
L.F. phase shifting.   The lower trace is the result
of damped oscillation*

distortion in this way, but this method of testing will reveal serious distortion, and will show on what part of the amplifier's transfer characteristic the distortion is occurring. Probably the main use of a triangular waveform when checking for distortion is for testing class B power amplifiers for excessive cross-over distortion. If a good quality input signal (as in the upper trace of Figure 2.18) emerges looking like the lower trace of Figure 2.18, severe cross-over distortion is present. A higher bias current through the output transistors is then needed. Even quite low levels of cross-over distortion can be detected if the oscilloscope's controls are adjusted to zoom-in on the appropriate part of the waveform.

Lissajous Figures
If your oscilloscope has an X input it is interesting to try displaying some lissajous figures. These are not particularly

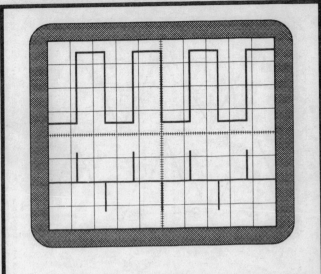

Fig.2.17 *If a squarewave (top) emerges looking something like the lower trace, faulty coupling is the most likely problem*

useful for general testing purposes, but are something that every oscilloscope owner should give a quick try out, just for the fun of it if for no other reason! If you simply connect the same signal to the X and Y inputs, you get a straight line sloping upwards from the bottom left hand corner of the screen to the top right hand corner. This must be the case, since any voltage that moves the spot in the X plane will be matched by an identical voltage (and therefore movement) in the Y plane. Assuming the X and Y sensitivities are the same, the line will be at an angle of 45 degrees. Any imbalance in the X and Y sensitivities or input levels will alter the angle of the line. The greater the relative deflection produced by the Y signal, the steeper the slope of the line.

If one of the signals is 180 degrees out-of-phase with the other, a straight line will again be obtained. However, this time it will slope from the bottom right hand corner of the

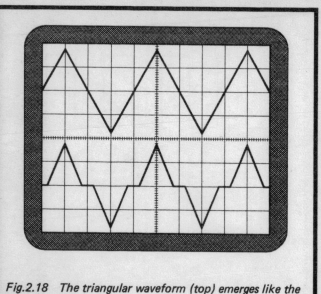

Fig.2.18   The triangular waveform (top) emerges like the
bottom trace if it is subjected to cross-over
distortion

screen to the top left hand corner. The traces obtained with
phase differences of zero and 180 degrees are shown in Figure
2.19. Of course, as with ordinary traces, the X and Y position
controls, and the sensitivity controls, must be adjusted to give
a suitable trace size and position on the screen.

The standard lissajous figure trick is to use two sinewave
signals that are 90 degrees out-of-phase. This gives a circular
trace, as in Figure 2.20. This assumes that the input levels and
the X/Y sensitivities are identical. Any imbalances will result
in a horizontal or vertical ellipse being produced. In order to
try out this effect you will need a phase shift network, but
this needs to be nothing more than a three stage resistor and
capacitor network used in the manner shown in Figure 2.21.
This will provide a range of phase shifts at frequencies from
a few hertz to a few kilohertz, and should give a circular trace
at about 200 hertz or so. This is potentially a useful method

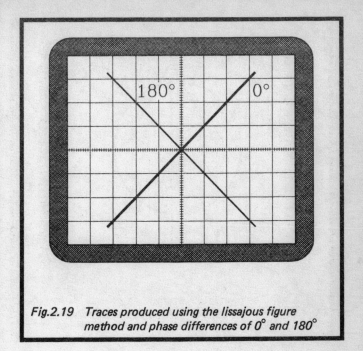

Fig.2.19 *Traces produced using the lissajous figure method and phase differences of 0° and 180°*

of measuring phase difference if you have a single beam oscilloscope. Unfortunately, results tend to be a bit difficult to interpret, but it will at least give a rough indication of the relative phasing of the two input signals.

The lissajous figure method can be used to show distortion. With two identical input signals the trace should be a straight line. Any distortion will kink or curve the line. As an example, the trace of Figure 2.22 would be obtained if one of the signals was subjected to mild and symmetrical clipping.

Logic Testing
An oscilloscope is well suited to much logic testing. The only real problem is that the signals in some logic circuits are at very high frequencies or are very brief in duration. Unless you have quite a high specification instrument this can result in them being undetectable. However, this is not a major problem

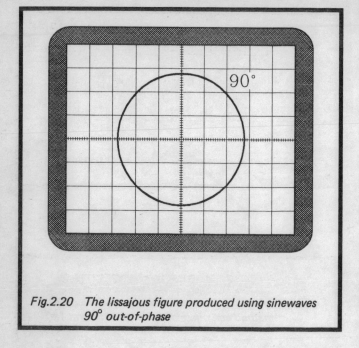

Fig.2.20 The lissajous figure produced using sinewaves 90° out-of-phase

as most logic circuits operate at frequencies that can be accommodated by a standard 20MHz workshop oscilloscope.

For logic testing the oscilloscope should be used with d.c. coupling so that the voltage levels in test circuits can be measured. You can then check that static points in the circuit are at legal voltages, and that dynamic signals are switching between valid voltage levels. The only point to note when testing dynamic signals is that the limitations of the oscilloscope must be kept in mind. On a high speed signal it might appear that it is not switching properly between valid logic 0 and logic 1 levels when the problem is due to the switching speed of the oscilloscope being inadequate to track the input signal properly.

Exactly what constitutes a legal logic voltage depends on the logic family and supply voltage in use. For CMOS integrated circuits it is not possible to give specific voltage ranges,

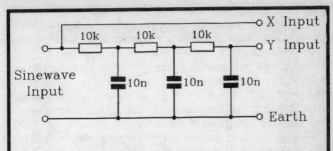

Fig.2.21 A simple phase shift network for producing lissajous figures

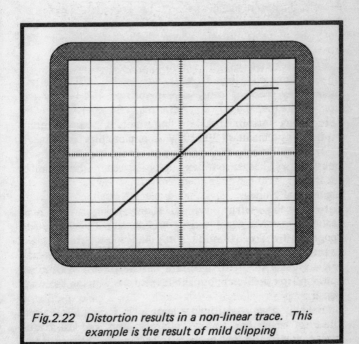

Fig.2.22 Distortion results in a non-linear trace. This example is the result of mild clipping

since these devices can operate at supply voltages of between about 3 and 18 volts. What is a perfectly valid logic 0 level at one supply voltage could be a legitimate logic 1 level with a much lower supply potential in use. In general terms, a logic 0 level should be between 0 and 30% of the supply voltage, while a logic 1 level should be in the range 70 to 100% of the supply voltage. With a 5 volt supply for example, an output set at logic 0 should be between 0 and 1.5 volts, while one at logic 1 should be between 3.5 and 5 volts.

With most CMOS outputs that are static or switching at low frequencies you will find that the two logic levels are virtually equal to the supply potentials. This is due to the complementary output stages used in CMOS logic devices, and the very high load resistance provided by these components. The situation is a little different if an output is switching at high speed or is loaded by something that consumes a significant amount of current (such as a l.e.d. for example). The signal may then fall well short of one or both supply potentials, and some careful measuring might be needed to determine whether or not the output is achieving acceptable voltages.

TTL integrated circuits are normally run from a 5 volt supply. Some TTL logic families, such as the 74HC** series, can actually work at other supply voltages, but in practice supplies of other than 5 volts seem to be very rarely used with TTL circuits. Assuming that a 5 volt supply is used, an output at logic 0 should be in the range 0 to 0.8 volts, and one at logic 1 should be from 2 to 5 volts. In most cases you will find that TTL logic outputs are well within these limits.

Logic Signal Tracing

With some logic circuits you can adopt an approach that is analogous to the signal tracing technique used with linear circuits. This type of testing is not always applicable to logic circuits though. Logic circuits that have a series of stages which process an input signal are relatively rare. This type of thing is not unknown, but about the only common example that springs to mind is a circuit that has a clock oscillator followed by a series of divider stages. Circuits of this type appear in such things as crystal calibrators and baud rate generators. If you have a circuit that consists of something like a 4MHz crystal oscillator plus a series of six divide by ten circuits, testing it should not be difficult.

The obvious first test is to ensure that the crystal oscillator is functioning properly. With a fairly modest input frequency of 4MHz the oscilloscope should permit you to measure the duration of one cycle so that a rough check on the input frequency can be made. Although you might think that with a crystal oscillator it would be a matter of the circuit either functioning properly or failing to operate at all, it may not be as clear cut as this. Some crystals give more lively oscillation than others, and with a low quality type it could be that the output of the circuit is there, but at a level that is just slightly too low to drive a logic circuit properly. Another potential problem with crystal oscillators is that of them oscillating at the wrong frequency! Crystals have a main resonant frequency, but often have others, generally at a figure that is harmonically related to their marked operating frequency. I have encountered several crystals which exhibited a definite tendency to oscillate at half their marked operating frequency.

With the aid of an oscilloscope it will usually be possible to check that suitable signal voltages are present, and that the output frequency is correct. The operating frequency will normally be spot on or nowhere near the correct figure, making precise frequency measurement unnecessary.

If a suitable output signal is found, it is then a matter of checking the output from each of the divider stages, working down the chain of stages until one which provides no output (or an incorrect signal of some kind) is found. If an incorrect output signal is found, then it is highly likely that the integrated circuit providing this signal is the cause of the problem. However, do not overlook the possibility that the problem is due to a fault at the input of the subsequent stage. The printed circuit boards for logic circuits are almost invariably very complex with a high component and track density. This gives a high risk of short circuits due to solder blobs, and the absence of any significant output signal often means that the output pin is short-circuited to one or other of the supply rails. A very low output signal level with valid logic levels not being achieved probably indicates that the output pin is short circuited to another output. If the signal is at valid logic levels, but is at the same frequency as the input signal, then the problem is almost certainly a faulty divider chip (a problem I have encountered on a few occasions).

Obviously much logic testing is a lot less straightforward than this. The signals are often irregular in nature, and might be very brief and infrequent. With any testing using an oscilloscope it is first a matter of determining what should be happening at various test points, and then investigating to find out just what is actually happening. The better your knowledge of the circuit, the greater your chance of successfully finding the location of the fault. Electronic projects often have fairly detailed circuit descriptions, and these are a useful source of information when servicing the project. If you do not have the requisite knowledge to follow a circuit description properly, there is usually a more broad description of the project, often aided by a block diagram. This should give a rough indication of the type of signal to be expected in each part of the circuit.

Where a signal is of an intermittent nature it might be necessary for you to arrange things so that the circuit generates a suitable signal for the oscilloscope to detect. With a keyboard circuit for instance, it might only produce serially coded output signals when a key is pressed. You would then have to press a few keys to ensure that an output signal was being produced, with a different pulse pattern being generated from each key. With a computer add-on which connects to the buses of the computer there is an address decoder circuit. This generates an enable pulse to activate the main circuit each time a read or write operation is performed. An obvious check for a circuit of this type is to perform test read and write operations, using the oscilloscope to determine whether or not the enable pulses are being produced.

This type of testing often requires the detection of very short pulses. As explained in Chapter 1, even with the brightness control set at maximum, very short pulses can give a very dim display, and might not give a visible trace at all if they are only very intermittent. When testing something like an address decoder, using a software routine to repeatedly write to the add-on at a high rate will effectively turn the enable pulses into a repetitive signal that can be more easily displayed.

If a technique of this type is not practical, it might be better to select a fairly long sweep time. You will not be able to view the input pulses properly, but each time an input pulse occurs the sweep generator will be activated, giving a clear flash from the oscilloscope's screen. In other words, you just use the oscilloscope as a pulse detector, and make no attempt to view the wave shape of the input signal.

Relative Timing

With logic circuits the relative timing of two or more signals is often of crucial importance. As a typical example, the timing of the signals on a computer's parallel port is crucial to the correct transfer of data. The usual arrangement is to have the eight parallel data lines plus a strobe output. When new data is present on the data lines a brief negative pulse is produced on the strobe output. This indicates to the receiving device that fresh data is present and must be acted upon. In most cases the strobe pulse is used to latch data into an eight bit data latch in the receiving equipment. A handshake output on the receiving device connects to the corresponding input on the computer's parallel port. This is needed in order to give a correctly regulated flow of data, with the computer not sending data at a higher rate than the receiving device can digest it.

A typical arrangement is for the handshake output to go high when a fresh byte of data has been received, and low again when this byte has been processed and the next one is awaited. The "Busy" line of a Centronics style printer port is an example of a handshake line of this type. An alternative form of handshaking is where the handshake output is normally high, and it is pulsed low each time a byte of data has been received and processed. This pulse indicates to the sending device that it is alright to output the next byte. The "Acknowledge" line of a Centronics type parallel port is an example of a handshake line of this kind. These are just two popular forms of handshaking, and obviously there are many possible variations on these basic schemes of thing.

For checking the relative timing of signals there is obviously a tremendous advantage in having a dual trace instrument. In fact it could be advantageous to have three or more channels if you are going to do a lot of checking on logic circuits. You do not actually need to have a separate channel for each signal you will measure, although it will probably be quicker and easier if you do. Assuming that just the usual two channels are available, the channel 1 input would be fed from the main signal in the group to be investigated. In our parallel port example, the strobe pulse is what would seem to be the important one, with all the others having to be correctly timed relative to this pulse. The strobe signal would therefore be connected to the channel 1 input. The other lines would then be connected to the channel 2 input, one at a time, so that their timing relative to the strobe pulse could be checked. When testing a handshake line, the result might be something along the lines of the traces shown in Figure 2.23. One point it is worth making is that timing diagrams in data sheets etc. show the signals as nice neat

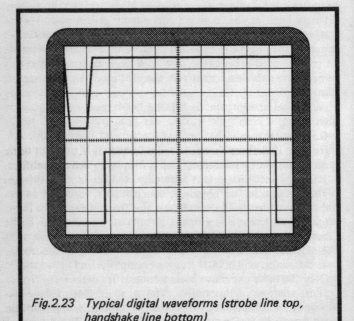

Fig.2.23 Typical digital waveforms (strobe line top, handshake line bottom)

waveforms. Do not be surprised if in practice there is a lot of noise on the signals, and the transitions from one state to the other are something less than instant and completely "clean".

If you have a single trace oscilloscope it might still be possible to measure the relative timing of two signals, but you will need an instrument that has an external trigger input. The basic idea is to trigger the sweep generator from the main signal, and to feed the other signal to the Y input. With our parallel port example, the trigger input would be fed from the strobe output, and would be set for negative edge triggering (i.e. to trigger on the leading edge of the negative strobe pulse). It is advisable to connect the strobe pulse to the Y input initially, so that its duration and voltage levels can be checked. The other signals are then connected to the Y input, in turn, until they have all been checked. Of course, this method can also be used with a dual trace instrument, permitting two lines at a time to be checked.

If you know what signals should be present in a logic circuit, then an oscilloscope will usually permit you to make precise checks on the actual signals present. Any discrepancies should then be quite apparent. If you do not have the necessary technical information and (or) expertise to support this method of checking, then you can still check that the signals present in the circuit are valid logic types, and an oscilloscope will still often bring the fault to light.

R.F. Signals
You can undertake checks on radio frequency equipment using much the same basic techniques as for testing audio amplifiers. There are some important differences to keep in mind though. The frequencies are obviously much higher, especially in the front-end circuits. In some cases the frequencies at the input (and possibly elsewhere in the circuit) may be too high to be detected on your oscilloscope. An ordinary broadcast band F.M. tuner for instance, will be dealing with input frequencies in the region of 100MHz in its r.f. amplifier and mixer stages. Only the more expensive oscilloscopes offer usable sensitivities at frequencies of this order. The standard intermediate frequency for equipment of this type is 10.7MHz, which is within the capabilities of most modern oscilloscopes. There is less of

a problem with a.m. broadcast receivers where the maximum input frequency is about 1.6MHz, and the intermediate frequency is usually about 460kHz.

Another point to bear in mind is that radio equipment will often function with input levels of only a few microvolts. In order to undertake signal tracing using an oscilloscope you must ensure that the input signal level is high enough in amplitude to be readily detectable by the oscilloscope. This will usually mean having a signal level that is ten or more times the minimum needed for the radio itself to function properly. You must avoid having very high input levels. The automatic gain control circuit would probably prevent overloading, but results could be difficult to interpret.

If the input frequency is low enough, and the sweep speed is high enough, the waveform of the radio frequency signal can be displayed. It is not essential to display the waveform though, and with a relatively long sweep speed a bar will be displayed across the screen. The height of the bar enables you to measure the peak to peak amplitude of the signal in the usual way (divide by 2.83 in order to give an answer in r.m.s. volts). Any clipping of the signal will be apparent as bright lines will appear along the top and bottom of the bar. This does, of course, assume that the bandwidth of the oscilloscope is good enough to show up any clipping properly.

If the signal is amplitude modulated and you display its waveform, the height of the waveform will be seen to jump up and down in sympathy with the modulation, or the waveform might just be rather blurred and indistinct. This depends on the nature of the audio modulation signal. If you set a low sweep rate the modulation will be clearly visible on the signal as variations in amplitude. The example of Figure 2.24 shows the result of a sinewave modulation signal with strong (but less than 100%) modulation. The only problem in obtaining a good quality display of this type is that it might be difficult to get the sweep generator to produce a stable display. Most oscilloscopes seem to be quite good in this respect though, and careful adjustment of the trigger level control will usually give good results.

Remember that the input impedance of an oscilloscope falls substantially at high frequencies. This will result in

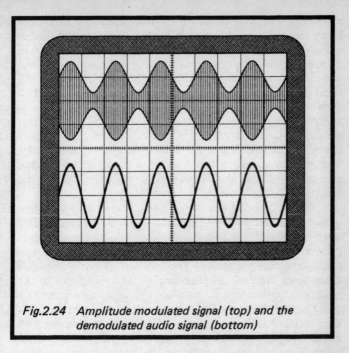

*Fig.2.24   Amplitude modulated signal (top) and the
demodulated audio signal (bottom)*

severe loading on high impedance circuits, and is likely to
cause significant detuning if the input signal is taken from
an L − C tuned circuit. Where possible try to test the signal
at low or medium impedance points in the circuit. It is
preferable to use an X10 probe for this type of testing, but the
reduction in sensitivity provided by one of these could give
problems when testing the input circuits.

Chapter 3

OTHER TEST GEAR

Although a multimeter and an oscilloscope can handle most electronic testing, there is a great deal to be said in favour of having other items of test equipment to back them up. If you do not have access to an oscilloscope, then there is even more to be said in favour of having a few other items of equipment to fill in the gaps in a multimeter's repertoire. As already explained, an oscilloscope is very good at locating the general area in which a fault lies, but it will not always pin down the exact cause of the problem. A multimeter can be used to undertake certain types of component testing and to provide continuity checks, and these will often show up the exact cause of the malfunction. It is useful to have equipment that can undertake component checks that are beyond the scope of the multimeter. If you do not have an oscilloscope, there are more simple pieces of equipment that can go some way to providing the same functions. The information they provide will usually be less precise, and in some cases a bit vague, but they will usually enable you to get the job done.

Component Testing

Ideally you should have the ability to check any component in any circuit that you have to service. In practice this is an unlikely state of affairs, since the range of components in common use these days is so vast. The bigger component catalogues list many thousands of items, and no single catalogue includes the full range of components currently available. A multimeter can be used to check resistors and diodes, and with the right techniques it is possible to check many other types of component as well. This subject is covered in some detail in BP239 and BP265, and is not something that will be considered further here.

One type of component that few multimeters can test properly is the humble capacitor. It is possible to make a few basic checks, such as ensuring that the test component has not gone short circuit. Thorough testing of capacitors is only possible with the few types that have built-in capacitance ranges. It is well worth obtaining a digital multimeter that includes facilities such as capacitance ranges and a good transistor tester function. The additional cost of an instrument which offers these facilities is often not very great, and buying separate transistor and capacitance testing units is likely to be very expensive. In fact, I found the cheapest way of buying a digital capacitance meter was to buy a digital multimeter with this function built-in! It does not cover quite the same range of values as the lower cost capacitance meters, and is probably slightly inferior in terms of its accuracy. However, it satisfies my requirements quite well, and at only about half the cost of the cheapest digital capacitance meter. It also includes an excellent built-in transistor gain check facility.

If you are interested in radio frequency equipment you may find that you need to check inductors from time to time. Few measuring instruments can measure inductance, and about the only type that can is the LCR bridge. As the name implies, a device of this type uses a bridge circuit to permit measurement of inductance, capacitance, and resistance. In most cases a wide range of values are covered on all three types of component. In use a bridge circuit is a bit crude when compared to modern digital equipment. A calibrated control knob is adjusted to give a null reading ⟨n a meter, or to null an audio tone. The value of the component is then read from the scale around the control knob. This may not seem to be a very sophisticated way of doing things, but it is a method that offers excellent accuracy over a very wide range of values with three different types of component.

If your budget does not run to things like digital capacitance meters and transistor checkers, do not overlook the possibility of building your own. There have been plenty of published designs for both types of unit, plus some good low cost analogue capacitance meter projects and measuring bridge circuits. Apart from increasing the capabilities of your test gear, units of this type represent very interesting projects to build.

Logic Testing

A logic probe is used for much the same sort of logic testing that is carried out using an oscilloscope. Even if you have an oscilloscope, it might still be worthwhile buying a logic probe. A device of this type will not give the same sort of detailed information as an oscilloscope, but it will often tell you what you need to know, and units of this type are quite small and inexpensive. When the sort of precise information provided by an oscilloscope is not needed, a logic probe represents what is usually a quicker and more convenient way of testing logic circuits. Even ready-made logic probes only cost a few pounds, and home constructor designs can often be largely built from "left overs", bringing the cost down to practically nothing.

In its most simple form a logic probe is just a passive device having two l.e.d. indicators. One switches on when the input is at logic 0 − the other comes on if the input is at logic 1. Units of this type are of limited value for several reasons. One of these is that they tend to load the test point quite heavily. This could easily result in a malfunction due to the presence of the probe, rather than a true fault at that point in the test circuit. Simple probes of this type are not very discriminating as far as acceptable input voltages are concerned. They tend to indicate valid input levels even when the input is well away from any legal logic voltage.

Finally, and perhaps most importantly, they do not give any proper pulse indication. Relatively long pulses will show up. If the input is predominantly in the low state, but occasionally pulses high for (say) 100ms, the "low" l.e.d. will light up, and each pulse will give a visible flash from the "high" l.e.d. If the input pulses are much shorter, but are very frequent, both l.e.d.s will seem to be continuously lit up, but at less than full brightness. The relative brightness gives an indication of the duty cycle of the input signal. For instance, if the "high" l.e.d. is much brighter than the "low" one, this indicates that the input signal is at the high state for a high proportion of the time.

The real problem is when the input signal is in the form of only very brief and occasional pulses. In most logic circuits there are plenty of signals of this kind. Because the pulses are so brief they will give flashes from the appropriate l.e.d. that are too brief for the eye to perceive properly. In fact it is quite likely that the l.e.d. will not respond to very short pulses

81

anyway. In either event, you are misled into thinking that the expected pulses are absent, when they may well be present and correct.

A good active logic probe will have "high" and "low" l.e.d. indicators, but they will be preceded by a circuit that will only activate the appropriate l.e.d. if the input voltage is genuinely within the acceptable range for that logic level. A good logic probe will also be switchable between TTL and CMOS modes of operation. Remember that the acceptable voltage ranges for each logic level are different for CMOS and TTL circuits. Also bear in mind that CMOS circuits often operate at supply voltages other than 5 volts. The logic probe should therefore be able to accommodate the full CMOS supply voltage range, or something very close to it.

Note that logic probes are almost invariably powered from the circuit under test via a pair of crocodile clip leads, and do not usually have a built-in battery supply. This ensures that they are powered from a suitable supply voltage, and that logic level incompatibilities due to different supply voltages are not allowed to creep in. As their current consumption is generally no more than about 20 milliamps this is not likely to give any problems. However, if a circuit has a power supply that is barely able to supply the unit properly, obviously the current drain of the logic probe could be the proverbial "last straw".

The pulse l.e.d. on a good quality active logic probe is driven via a pulse stretcher circuit. This will provide an output pulse to the l.e.d. of (typically) about 100ms regardless of the input pulse duration. This ensures that the l.e.d. flashes visibly even if the input pulse is less than a microsecond. In practice the unit will not respond to input pulses of less than a certain duration, but this duration should be very short (about 20ns or less). As an alternative to pulse stretching, some logic probes have a memory circuit. Some logic probes, including the one I use, can be switched between memory and pulse stretching operation. The memory mode latches the pulse l.e.d. when an input pulse occurs, so that there is absolutely no risk of an input pulse being overlooked. This mode could be useful when testing something that provides one-off pulses, such as the address decoder in a computer add-on project.

A few logic probes have a built-in "beeper". This gives a

low pitched "buzzing" sound if the input goes to logic 0, and a higher pitched "beep" sound if it is taken to logic 1. There may be a third sound to indicate that there is a pulsing input signal. This enables tests to be made without having to repeatedly look backwards and forwards between the l.e.d. indicators and the test points. It is not a facility that I have ever found to be particularly useful though, and it could make you unpopular with other people in the immediate vicinity.

In Use

In use a logic probe is utilized in much the same way as an oscilloscope. You can check that static levels are at the correct state, at legal voltages, and are not pulsing. You can check that pulse signals are pulsing properly, and with most probes you can also check that the duty cycle is approximately correct. With a divider circuit for example, the output is usually a good quality squarewave having a 1 to 1 mark-space ratio. If the probe indicates the mark-space ratio using the relative brightness of the "high" and "low" l.e.d.s, then the two l.e.d.s should be at the same brightness. On the probe I use the "pulse" l.e.d. varies in brightness, with high brightness indicating a high mark-space ratio. With a probe of this type, a 1 to 1 mark-space ratio would therefore give half brightness from the "pulse" l.e.d.

One advantage of a good logic probe over an oscilloscope is that the logic probe can detect very brief pulses that are too brief for some oscilloscopes to pick up. In general though, a logic probe is less informative, and might give misleading results on occasions. You need to bear their limitations in mind. Probably the main one is that the pulse indication does not give any really precise information about the input signal. You can detect that a pulse signal is present at the output of a divider stage, and that its duty cycle is approximately as expected, but unless the output is at a very low frequency so that you can see the "high" and "low" l.e.d.s flashing on and off, you have no real idea of the output frequency. If the pulse signal is absent altogether, then the probe will detect this state of affairs and you will then know that there is definitely a fault at that point in the test circuit. A pulse signal that appears to be correct may not be though, and you need to keep this possibility in mind. With any electronic servicing it is important to realise the difference between reasoned conclusions and jumping to conclusions.

Logic Pulsers

A logic pulser is a device that generates pulse trains that can be injected into a test circuit. They are often in the form of simple probe type tools which look very much like a logic probe. The output signal is often limited to brief pulses with (typically) two switched output frequencies (one at a few hundred pulses per second, and one at less than one pulse per second). These pulsers are often designed to inject a signal into a test circuit without having to remove any integrated circuits from the test circuit. Normally it is not acceptable to have two logic outputs connected together, as a high current could flow if they should adopt opposite states. This could easily damage one or both outputs. To inject a signal into a logic circuit it would normally be necessary to remove the integrated circuit that provides the drive signal at that point in the circuit. Some logic pulsers get around this problem by using an output circuit that "crowbars" the test point to the opposite logic state, but only for a very short period of time (typically about 1 to 10μs). Although quite a high output current might flow during each output pulse, the short and relatively infrequent nature of the signal apparently prevents any damage from occurring.

More sophisticated pulsers are in the form of standard bench-top units, and often permit a very wide range of pulse durations and repetition rates to be set. If you want something like a 2μs pulse every 250ms, then a good logic pulser will probably be able to oblige. These normally provide an output signal at standard logic levels, and do not provide a "crowbar" output facility. Whereas the probe type pulsers are mainly intended for testing faulty logic circuits, these more sophisticated units are primarily intended for logic circuit development.

A sophisticated logic pulse generator is certainly very useful for someone who is involved in the design of digital circuits. For general service work on logic circuits I can not claim to have found either sophisticated or simple probe type pulsers to be particularly useful. Devices for detecting pulses, such as an oscilloscope or logic probe, seem to be of more use for this type of thing. I suppose that a logic pulser is analogous to a signal injector or generator for testing audio circuits. The important difference is that whereas there are countless items of equipment that take in an audio signal and amplify it or process it in some other way, there are few circuits that provide a comparable action with logic signals. Most logic circuits generate their own pulse signals. If the pulses are absent, then this in itself is a good indication of the source of the problem (i.e. whatever stage should be originating the missing signals is probably faulty). You do not often need to inject pulses into a digital circuit in order to test signal processing stages.

For the ultimate in logic testing the device to use is a logic analyser. These can monitor several signals at once, and record the input signals into memory so that they can be played back and examined in detail via what is usually an oscilloscope type display. While an instrument of this type is highly desirable, it is also very expensive. Units of this type usually have four figure price tags, and as yet, are not realistic possibilities for most electronic hobbyists.

A.F. Signal Generator

If you are interested in building audio equipment, then an audio signal generator should be high on your "hit list" of equipment. There are two basic types to choose from, which are the traditional sinewave/squarewave type, and the more modern function generator variety. A function generator usually has three output waveforms, which are triangular, sine, and squarewave. In fact the squarewave output is replaced with a variable pulse width output signal on some instruments. These usually have a pulse width control which gives a narrow positive pulse at one extreme, a squarewave signal at a central setting, and a long positive pulse at the other extreme (Figure 3.1).

The difference between traditional types and function generators is not merely the output waveforms they provide. They operate in substantially different fashions. A conventional signal generator is based on a high quality $C - R$

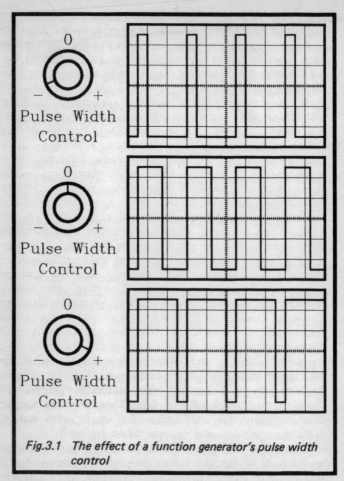

Fig.3.1 The effect of a function generator's pulse width control

oscillator, usually of the Wien network type and having thermistor stabilisation of its feedback. This gives a very high quality output, and even cheap instruments of this type mostly have distortion levels of well under 1% at most frequencies. The more expensive instruments often achieve distortion levels of something more like 0.005% over much of the audio frequency range. With a suitable filter these are suitable for measuring total harmonic distortion levels on high quality audio equipment. The squarewave signal is derived from the sinewave signal via a squaring amplifier or a trigger circuit. The squarewave output is often something of an afterthought, but with a suitable amplifier or trigger circuit a high quality output signal can be produced.

A function generator is based on a triangular oscillator, and this normally operates using two constant current generators which alternately charge and discharge a capacitor. The constant current gives a linear rate of charge/discharge, and a high quality linear triangular waveform is produced. The squarewave or pulse signal can be derived from the triangular signal using an amplifier or trigger circuit. This is essentially the same way in which the squarewave signal is produced in a traditional signal generator.

The sinewave signal is also derived from the triangular signal, and this is achieved using an amplifier which has a non-linear transfer characteristic. The gain of the amplifier reduces somewhat on positive and negative signal peaks. This results in a rounding of the peaks, giving something approximating to a sinewave output signal. Some function generators are more successful than others in this rounding off process. Good quality units can achieve distortion levels that are well under 1% at most frequencies, but the more simple units often have harmonic distortion levels of a few percent. Also, when the waveforms are viewed on an oscilloscope, with the cheaper function generators there are often noticeable "glitches" on the waveform. Despite these limitations, even the simpler function generators are suitable for much audio testing, including most frequency response measurements.

These days there is a third kind of audio signal generator in the form of digital function generators. These use digital techniques to produce the output waveforms, and can usually manage quite a repertoire, including such things as two types of sawtooth waveform, plus possibly something a bit more exotic such as a noise output signal. Equipment of this type tends to be quite expensive at present though, and is probably not a practical proposition for most amateur users.

The obvious question to ask is "what type of signal generator is best for audio testing?" If you need a high quality sinewave signal for distortion measurement, or perhaps highly accurate frequency response measurement even on high slope filters, then a good quality conventional instrument is almost certainly the best choice. For general audio testing you should find that either type is quite acceptable. My preference is for a conventional Wien oscillator type, but this is possibly due to the fact that this is the type I was (electronically speaking) brought up on, rather than this type having any real advantage. What is likely to be the deciding factor is cost. Looking through a few catalogues and studying prices, the average cost of function generators seems to be substantially higher than that for a good basic traditional instrument. Admittedly the function generators mostly seem to have one or two extra features, such as a digital frequency readout, but these will not necessarily be of much use to you in practice.

Sweep Generators

There is yet another form of audio signal generator called a "sweep oscillator" or "sweep generator". Usually this is a function generator plus some additional circuitry that permits the output frequency to be voltage controlled. Strictly speaking, a sweep generator does not need to have a built-in low frequency oscillator to control the output frequency. In practice though, this circuit is normally an integral part of the sweep oscillator, and it will often provide a choice of linear or logarithmic sweeps.

The idea of a sweep generator is to provide automatic measurement of frequency response using an arrangement of the type shown in Figure 3.2. There are various ways of ensuring that the sweep generator and the oscilloscope's sweep circuit are properly synchronised, but the most simple one is to have a sawtooth sweep signal output on the sweep generator that can be coupled to the X input of the oscilloscope. With the two instruments then using the same timebase circuit, there is obviously no way that any lack of synchronisation accuracy can creep in. Another arrangement is to have a trigger output on the sweep generator that can be used to drive the trigger input of the oscilloscope. The sweep rate controls of the oscilloscope must then be adjusted to synchronise the two timebases.

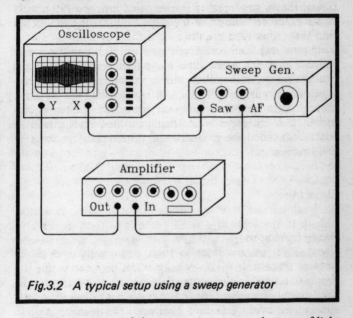

Fig.3.2 *A typical setup using a sweep generator*

The basic action of the system is to move the spot of light across the screen as the output frequency of the sweep generator is steadily moved upwards. The output of the sweep generator is fed through the test circuit and into the Y input of the oscilloscope. The height of the trace therefore depends on the gain of the test circuit, and is proportional to it. The trace is in the form of a bar across the screen, and this is effectively a graph of the test circuit's frequency response. The Y axis represents gain, while the X axis represents frequency. Using a chart recorder instead of an oscilloscope, and with everything carefully set up, it is possible to obtain accurate frequency response graphs automatically, and quite rapidly. When a sweep generator is used with an oscilloscope it is generally only to give a relatively rough indication of the test device's frequency response. It will, for example, almost instantly show up changes in frequency response when tone controls are adjusted, and should show up any deficiencies in their control range. It will also rapidly show up any unacceptable irregularities in the frequency response of a filter, such as the excessive "hump" in the response that can easily occur with some types of active filter.

If you own an oscilloscope and are likely to do a fair amount of audio testing, then a signal generator with a good sweep facility is definitely worth considering. The extra expenditure will probably be well worthwhile, but the extra money might be better spent on other items of test equipment. It really depends on whether or not funds extend to cover both the sweep generator and other important items of test equipment.

Signal Injector

A signal injector is a very crude form of signal generator, usually in the form of a small probe type tool. It is a very simple device which basically just generates a squarewave signal at a frequency of about 1kHz, and usually at an amplitude of a few volts peak to peak. The point of having the unit generate a squarewave (apart from the fact that this type of signal is easy to generate) is that it gives an output that is rich in harmonics. This provides signals at frequencies of up to at least a few megahertz, enabling the unit to be used for testing both audio and radio frequency equipment.

Although a signal injector has the virtues of being small, light, inexpensive and quite versatile, it also has some major drawbacks. Trying to track down even quite severe distortion borders on the impossible using a squarewave input signal, since this signal is very rich in harmonics. A clipped squarewave is still a squarewave! The other main problem is that most signal injects have no means of controlling the output level. This means that the output signal will overload many audio devices, and misleading results can be obtained with the signal breaking through stages where a fault would normally result in the signal being blocked. A signal injector is better than nothing, but it is no real substitute for a proper signal generator.

A.F. Testing

The basic techniques for fault finding on audio equipment were discussed in Chapter 2. If you do not have an oscilloscope, it is still possible to use the same basic techniques, but some form of signal tracer is needed to take the place of the oscilloscope. Ready-made signal tracers do not seem to be readily available any more, but as a unit of this type is essentially just a high gain audio amplifier driving a loudspeaker or headphones, building your own is not too difficult. There have been plenty of designs for units of this type published in the past, and practically any reasonably sensitive audio amplifier could be pressed into service for this application.

For a really low cost solution you only need a crystal earphone, a crocodile clip, and a test prod. Remove the miniature jack plug from the earphone lead, connect the crocodile clip to one wire, and the test prod to the other wire. In use, the crocodile clip lead connects to the earth rail of the equipment under test, and the test prod is connected to the various test points. A crystal earphone offers good sensitivity, and will permit signals down to a few millivolts to be heard. It has a fairly high input impedance and an extremely high input resistance. Therefore, it will not significantly load the test points, or upset the d.c. bias levels.

To undertake signal tracing you do not actually need to use a signal generator, and the ordinary signal source for the equipment will suffice. You may find it better to use the normal signal source, or you might prefer to use a sinewave test signal. As pointed out in Chapter 2, the normal signal source does have the advantage of ensuring that the input level to the equipment is at an appropriate level. On the other hand, it might not always be convenient, or even possible, to use the normal signal source.

Either way you should be able to hear even quite low levels of distortion on the signal if this should be the main problem, rather than a lack of gain. In this respect a sinewave signal is probably better, and most people can readily detect very small amounts of distortion on the very pure sound of a sinewave signal. When the problem is distortion occurring somewhere in the signal chain, there is obviously an advantage in having a signal tracer that is based on a good quality amplifier.

When searching for the source of distortion it is usually better to use headphones rather than the signal tracer's loudspeaker. Even quite inexpensive headphones seem to offer vastly better audio quality than the miniature loudspeakers used in most signal tracers, and for reasons I can not claim to understand, imperfections in signals seem to be more readily detectable using headphones even if everything is equal in other respects. With either type of signal source you should be able to roughly gauge the amount of voltage gain through a stage, but this is something where experience certainly helps a great deal. This is another respect in which a sinewave signal might be superior, with any changes in volume being more apparent, and easily judged with a simple test signal of this type.

As an alternative to a signal tracer you might consider an audio millivolt meter. This is merely an a.c. voltmeter, but one which can measure voltages down to a few millivolts. In fact most instruments of this type can accurately measure signals of well under 1 millivolt r.m.s. The bandwidth encompasses at least the full audio range, and most units of this type have upper $-3dB$ limits that are well into the radio frequency range. With a device of this type you can accurately measure signal levels at various points in the circuit. Like an oscilloscope, this enables the voltage gain of each stage to be measured precisely. By measuring the output level of a circuit over a wide range of test frequencies you can plot accurate frequency response charts for filters, tone controls, etc. You can also measure background noise levels so that the signal to noise ratio of equipment can be calculated.

An audio millivolt meter is a very useful piece of equipment for the audio project enthusiast, especially for someone who does not own an oscilloscope. Units of this type do have a few drawbacks though. The main one is simply that readymade a.c. millivolt meters tend to be very expensive. They are mostly very-sophisticated instruments which have specifications that go well beyond most amateur requirements. Audio millivolt meter projects are published from time to time though, and one of these projects could provide you with a very useful piece of test gear that will probably have quite a modest cost. You would also get the fun of building the unit!

Remember that a millivolt meter only tells you what signal level is present at the test point — it gives no indication if there is any distortion present. For this reason it is advisable to use a unit of this type in conjunction with a device that can detect distortion, which means having an oscilloscope or signal tracer as well. If you already have an oscilloscope then an audio millivolt meter is probably not going to increase the capabilities of your test equipment to any great degree. On the other hand, a signal tracer plus an audio millivolt meter is quite a powerful combination, and a good low cost substitute for an oscilloscope when undertaking audio service work.

R.F. Equipment

If you have an interest in radio frequency equipment, then there are one or two items of equipment that will prove to be more than a little useful to you. Much r.f. testing and alignment work requires signals at certain frequencies. You can get away with using radio stations on known frequencies for some testing and alignment purposes, but it is much more convenient and reliable to use a calibrated r.f. signal generator. These vary enormously in cost and sophistication, but a good workshop type is not too expensive, and will cater for most amateur requirements. A unit of this type would typically cover from about 100kHz to 150MHz in about half a dozen ranges (probably offering frequencies up to about 400 or 500MHz using harmonics of the fundamental signal).

With the less sophisticated units the output level changes quite dramatically with changes in output frequency. This type of thing is not acceptable with an audio signal generator, but with an r.f. type it is normally a signal on a certain frequency that is required, with the exact output level not being too important. Unfortunately, the dial calibration is not likely to be particularly accurate either, with errors of a few percent being quite typical.

If you need to have a signal on a certain frequency with a high degree of accuracy, then a digital frequency meter (d.f.m.) is required. You simply feed a signal to its input, and the frequency of the signal is displayed on the multi-digit display. A d.f.m. for r.f. use will be crystal controlled, and will offer very good accuracy (typically about 0.001%). Apart from use as a highly accurate digital readout for an r.f. signal generator, a d.f.m. can also be used to measure the frequency of oscillators in circuits being tested. Accuracy might then be compromised by loading effects, and where possible the signal should be tapped off from a low impedance part of the circuit.

This is especially important when measuring the frequency of an L − C oscillator. Placing the input capacitance of the d.f.m. across the tuning capacitance of the oscillator could easily have a very large detuning effect on the oscillator. Most d.f.m.s are designed to have a high input impedance and low input capacitance so that loading effects are minimised. Typical figures would be about 1 megohm and 25pF respectively. However, a high frequency L − C oscillator could have a tuning capacitance of only about 10 to 30pF, and shunting about 25pF across this will obviously have a radical effect on the output frequency. Even an inexpensive d.f.m. will offer good sensitivity, giving reliable operation with input levels of (typically) down to about 30 millivolts r.m.s. This enables them to be driven from practically any oscillator, even if the input signal is taken from a low impedance part of the circuit (where the signal level will normally be much lower than the signal amplitude across the tuned circuit).

The cost of d.f.m.s varies enormously, and their prices are largely determined by the maximum input frequency they can accommodate, and the number of digits in their display. Low cost types seem to cover frequencies up to about 50MHz, which is adequate for many purposes. If you are interested in v.h.f. and u.h.f. equipment a much higher maximum usable frequency will be desirable. Units covering up to 1GHz (1000MHz) are readily available, but cost about 50 to 100% more than low cost instruments.

Units that offer frequency measurement beyond about 50MHz mostly operate using a device called a "prescaler". This is a circuit that divides the input frequency by a certain amount, which in practice normally means a division by 10 or 100. If you have an ordinary 50MHz d.f.m. and you add a divide by ten circuit ahead of it, provided the divider circuit is of adequate quality, input frequencies of up to 500MHz can be accommodated. A minor drawback of an external prescaler is that it results in a displayed frequency that is only one-tenth of the true figure, and some simple mental arithmetic is needed in order to convert the displayed figure to the actual input frequency. Of course, if a d.f.m. has an integral prescaler, then the range switching automatically switches the decimal point so that the display always indicates the input frequency correctly.

A slight drawback of using a prescaler is that it reduces the resolution of the unit. If a d.f.m. uses a gate period of one-tenth of a second, it will have a resolution of 10Hz. Adding a divide by 10 prescaler ahead of the instrument means that in order to produce a 10Hz minimum resolution reading, a 100Hz input is required. This reduces the resolution to 100Hz, and with a divide by 100 prescaler it would be further reduced by a factor of ten (i.e. 1kHz resolution). On the other hand, when you are measuring frequencies of a few hundred megahertz, relatively low resolution may well be perfectly acceptable.

It might appear that the resolution of inexpensive d.f.m.s is limited by the number of digits in the display rather than the gate period. In practice this is often not the case. Although a 50MHz d.f.m. having a 4 digit display might seem to have a 10kHz resolution, most units of this type offer several measuring ranges. Using a system known as "over-ranging" it is then possible to effectively increase the number of digits in the display. Suppose that on the 50MHz range an input signal gives a reading of 12.34MHz. Switching down to the 5MHz range then gives a reading of 2.345MHz, and then switching to the 500kHz range gives a reading of 345.6kHz. Each time you switch down a range the most significant digit is lost, but you gain an extra digit at the low end of the readout.

The digits that are lost at the high end of the readout do not matter, since you have already determined these when taking readings on the higher ranges. By adding together the digits obtained from the readings you can get the best of both worlds, with both high maximum readings and good resolution being obtained. In our above example we obtained an initial reading of 12.34MHz and subsequent readings added least significant digits of 5 and 6. This gives a total reading of 12.3456MHz. In other words, six digit accuracy has been obtained from a four digit display. Incidentally, although this system works perfectly well with most multi-range d.f.m.s, it is not usable with most other forms of digital measuring instrument.

Crystal Calibrators

An alternative and inexpensive method of obtaining highly accurate calibration frequencies is to use a device called a crystal calibrator. In its most simple form this is a circuit that provides a single and highly accurate output frequency. Virtually all modern crystal calibrators have several output frequencies, often with the aid of digital divider circuits rather than having numerous switched crystals. A typical crystal calibrator would provide output frequencies at something like 10MHz, 5MHz, 2MHz, 1MHz, 500kHz, 200kHz, 100kHz, 50kHz, 20kHz, and 10kHz.

This may not seem to be particularly useful, but bear in mind that apart from these fundamental frequencies, a unit of this type is also designed to provide harmonics at frequencies of up to 30MHz, and possibly into the v.h.f. range. The 100kHz output for example, will therefore provide calibration signals at 100kHz intervals throughout the long, medium, and shortwave bands. The only problem is that with an uncalibrated receiver, how do you tell which calibration frequency is which? The trick is to initially use a fairly high fundamental frequency. The fundamental and harmonic signals are then well spread out, and there is little risk of mistaking one signal for another.

Suppose you need a calibration frequency at 14.35MHz for instance. You could first select a 5MHz fundamental signal, and then locate the third harmonic at 15MHz. You would then switch to a fundamental frequency of 500kHz, and tune the receiver lower in frequency until the next calibration signal was found. This would be 500kHz below 15MHz, or 14.5MHz in other words. Next the fundamental frequency would be switched to 50kHz, and the receiver would be tuned down to the next calibration signal (14.45MHz), then the next

(14.4MHz) and finally to the next, which would be the required 14.35MHz.

A calibration oscillator may not be the most convenient form of r.f. signal source to use, but it does have attractions. Probably the main one is that it is a relatively cheap way of obtaining a wide range of calibration frequencies. It also has the advantage of providing extremely accurate results.

Dip Meters

There are a number of other r.f. test instruments in common use, and how much test equipment of this type you need obviously depends on the depth of your interest in radio related projects and equipment. A grid dip meter is a popular piece of test equipment amongst radio enthusiasts, and is perhaps the most useful of these other r.f. test devices. Grid dip meters are also known as a gate dip meter, which is a more accurate description of modern units that are based on field effect transistors rather than thermionic valves. Just plain "dip meter" now seems to be gaining in popularity. Whatever the name, the function of a device of this type is to detect the resonant frequency of a tuned circuit without any connection actually being made to that circuit.

The standard form for a dip meter is a hand held box with a coil holder at the top. You plug in the coil for the range of frequencies that are of interest, and place the coil near to the tuned circuit you wish to test. You then adjust the tuning control to obtain a null reading on the meter, and read off the resonant frequency of the tuned circuit on the tuning scale. Most dip meters offer a range of useful extra features, and can operate as a simple r.f. signal generator, accept crystals for spot frequency generation, have a built-in modulation oscillator with an audio output, etc. A good dip oscillator is a very versatile piece of test equipment that does not cost a great deal.

I will not go into the subject of aligning receivers here, since the procedure differs substantially from one receiver to another. For a home constructor design the book or article should include concise details of the alignment procedure, as should the service manual for a ready-made receiver. Do not try to align a receiver unless you are absolutely certain you know what you are doing. The alignment procedure for some modern communications equipment is an involved process which requires specialised equipment. With a receiver of this type it is advisable to leave its alignment in the hands of authorised service centres.

Power Supplies
For anyone interested in electronics as a hobby I would recommend that a good bench power supply should be one of the first items of test equipment that they purchase. Many electronic projects are battery powered, and you can obviously use batteries when testing them. However, it is surprising how quickly you can go through sets of batteries when servicing equipment. This can be a very expensive method of powering equipment in the medium to long term. With projects that have a built-in mains power supply, when testing them it is often easier (and safer) to remove the main circuit boards from the case and then power them from a bench power supply. It is my standard practice to test all newly constructed boards in this way prior to fitting them into the case and wiring them up to the rest of the unit. This may be a waste of time, and the board might work perfectly. However, if the board is faulty, and many newly constructed boards contain minor faults, it is relatively quick and easy to sort out the problems at this stage of the proceedings. If you intend to develop your own circuits, then a bench power supply is virtually a necessity.

The greater the output voltage range and output current the supply can provide, the more useful it will be. On the other hand, the cost of power supplies seems to escalate rapidly as the specification rises, and you need to think carefully about the type of project you will power from the unit, and the sort of output power you will really need. If you are only likely to test low power projects that can be easily accommodated by a 1 amp supply, there would seem to be little point in paying out for a 3 amp type. If you are interested in audio power amplifiers, then a supply having relatively high maximum output voltage and current ratings is likely to be a decided asset. If you are not interested in audio power amplifiers, or other high power circuits, then a supply having a specification of something like 0 to 20 volts at currents of up to 1 amp should be perfectly adequate.

With so many circuits based on logic devices these days, and requiring a 5 volt supply, it is important to have a supply that can be adjusted down to 5 volts or less. Fortunately, most modern power supply units seem to be adjustable right down to zero volts.

A few power supplies offer dual balanced or dual individually adjustable supplies. These are suitable for circuits that require twin supplies with a central 0 volt rail, which mainly means d.c. coupled circuits based on operational amplifiers. Although this type of circuit was commonplace at one time, relatively few modern circuits use twin supplies. Improvements in operational amplifiers and circuit designs mean that it is often possible to produce single supply circuits where twin supply versions would once have been required. This makes a dual supply less of an asset that it once was.

It is still a worthwhile feature to have, but twin supplies usually means about double the cost. A more economic solution is to have a single supply unit having good maximum supply voltages and currents, and to build a twin supply which has relatively restricted output voltages and currents. Designs for these are published from time to time, and they are not expensive to build. Most circuits that require dual supplies have modest current requirements, and a simple dual supply will suffice for most purposes. Do not overlook the possibility of building your own main bench supply unit. This is a type of project where the home constructed variety is often substantially cheaper than a ready-made alternative.

Most bench power supplies offer quite good performance. Ideally the ripple on the output should be no more than about 1 millivolt r.m.s., and most units now seem to offer only about half that level. In specifications you will see references to "load" and "line" regulation. This is the change in output voltage (as a percentage) for a given change in the output current and input voltage respectively. Modern voltage regulators are so good that in most cases the change in output voltage will be no more than a small fraction of 1% provided the input voltage and output current are kept within the normal operating ranges.

An essential feature for any bench power supply is some

form of overload protection. Short circuits and overloads are likely to occur quite frequently. Normal fuses are inadequate as they might not "blow" fast enough to protect the supply, and frequently replacing them would be a bit tedious and expensive. The standard form of loverload protection for modern supply units is current limiting. This simply prevents the output current from more than marginally exceeding the maximum output current rating of the supply. If the output is short circuited, the output voltage almost immediately falls to little more than zero volts, and the output current is limited to something like 10% more than the maximum current rating of the supply.

This is a very effective method of protecting the power supply itself from damage, but it might not give much protection to the circuit you are powering from the unit. A small project might have a normal current consumption of only a few milliamps, whereas the short circuit output current of the supply would typically be around 1 to 3 amps. If a fault in the project caused an excessive supply current to flow, the current limiting of the power supply might not come into action, and would not prevent a grossly excessive supply current from flowing even if it did.

Fortunately, some form of adjustable current limiting seems to be a standard feature these days. This might be in the form of several switched current limit levels, but is more usually a continuously adjustable control that enables virtually any desired limit current to be set. If the test circuit has a normal current consumption of (say) 10 milliamps, the limit current would be set somewhat above this figure (about 15 to 20 milliamps would do). This should ensure that there is no risk of an excessive supply current causing any damage to delicate semiconductors in the test circuit.

When using a bench power supply try to avoid the two classic mistakes. The first of these is simply getting the supply polarity wrong. Connection to the test circuit is usually via a pair of crocodile clips, with no battery connector to ensure that the supply polarity is correct. Modern semiconductors are less vulnerable to reversed power supplies than those of about twenty years ago. The germanium devices used in those days were almost instantly destroyed by a supply of the wrong polarity. Many modern semi-conductors can withstand this error without damage. However, some of the more complex and expensive devices are vulnerable to this error. Some devices are not destroyed by the reverse polarity supply as such, but will draw a high current supply current and could quickly overheat and become damaged. The power supply's current limiting might prevent this, but it is better to carefully check the supply polarity and get it right first time.

The second classic mistake is to connect the supply, switch it on, and then set its output voltage. If the supply was left with the output at about 15 volts, and you are using it to supply a 5 volt circuit using TTL logic chips, it would be reasonable to expect all the integrated circuits in the test unit to be destroyed by the time you have adjusted the supply down to the correct level of 5 volts! It is a wise precaution to always adjust the output voltage down to a low level each time you finish using the power supply.

Index